MORE THINGS *in* HEAVEN *and* EARTH

Poets and Astronomers Read the Night Sky

David H. Levy

David H. Levy (signature)

The Wombat Press

Published by The Wombat Press
P.O. Box 282
Wolfville, Nova Scotia
Canada B0P 1X0

The publisher gratefully acknowledges the support of the
Nova Scotia Department of Education and Culture,
Cultural Affairs Division.

The publisher acknowledges with thanks permission to
reproduce the following images:
Robert Frost: Copyright Ray Fisher.
Henry D. Thoreau: courtesy of The Thoreau Society,
    Lincoln, MA.
Portrait of Galileo Galilei: Ottavio Leoni; collection of the
    Art Gallery of Ontario, Toronto; gift of Stillman and
    Florence Drake.
Nicholas Copernicus: The Bettman Archive 409.03.
Francis Bacon: The Bettman Archive SF1046.
Alfred Lord Tennyson: Corbis-Bettman SF15953.
Gerard Manley Hopkins: Rita MacKenzie

Cover design: Steven Slipp
Interior design: Margo Grant
Back cover author photo: Dan Callis
Printed and bound by: McCurdy Printing

Canadian Cataloguing in Publication Data

Levy, David H. (David Howard), 1948-

More things in heaven and earth.

Includes bibliographical references and index.

1. Astronomy in literature. I. Title.

PN1059.S3 L48 1997   821.009'36   C97-950126-1

Twinkle, twinkle, little star,
How I wonder what you are!
Up above the world so high,
Like a diamond in the sky.

When the blazing sun is gone,
When he nothing shines upon,
Then you show your little light,
Twinkle, twinkle, all the night.

Then the trav'ller in the dark,
Thanks you for your tiny spark,
He could not see which way to go,
If you did not twinkle so.

In the dark blue sky you keep,
And often thro' my curtains peep,
For you never shut your eye,
Till the sun is in the sky.

'Tis your bright and tiny spark,
Lights the trav'ller in the dark:
Tho' I know not what you are,
Twinkle, twinkle, little star.

Jane Taylor, *The Star*, 1806 [A]

This photograph of the Milky Way, taken
by the author a few days before his co-
discovery of Comet Shoemaker-Levy 9,
accompanies the most famous astronomical poem in the English language. The
star at the top is Vega, in the constellation of Lyra.

FOR WENDEE

Who gave me the greatest gift,
the opportunity to share our lives.

Contents

What is it all but a trouble of ants in the gleam of a million million of suns?

Tennyson, *Vastness* [B]

The Whirlpool Galaxy is an example of a great spiral galaxy viewed face-on from Earth. Tim Hunter photo.

Acknowledgements

The seed for this book was planted in 1970, as I daydreamed in Roger Lewis's Victorian Poetry class at Acadia University. We were reading *In Memoriam*, and Roger pointed out Tennyson's incredible grasp of the science of his time. Throughout these intervening years, I have always appreciated that moment when I first became aware of the interplay between science and poetry. A quarter century later, Roger and I discussed the idea of a nonscholarly book aimed at showing this relationship. Had it not been for our continuing friendship, I probably would never have thought of writing this book.

In 1978, Norman MacKenzie, of Queen's University, Kingston, introduced me to Gerard Manley Hopkins's poetic fragment "I am like a slip of comet." More than any other piece of literature I have read, I consider these lines to contain the real substance of the relation of astronomy to literature. I thank Norman again for his careful suggestions on chapters 4 and 5 of this book.

I want to thank Steven Slipp for his invaluable suggestions regarding the content, design, and production, and to Margo Grant for her page design and layout. Jan Williams's copyediting was superb; it sharpened the prose and the flow. Additionally, I thank Joan-ellen Rice for providing useful information; Mary Lou and David Henry for commenting on the first chapter; and Acadia President Kelvin Ogilvie for contributing the Foreword. Finally, a special hug for my wife, Wendee, whose help with copyediting was invaluable, and whose love and encouragement throughout the writing of this book enabled me to bring it to completion.

Have I been gazing on the western sky,
  And its peculiar tint of yellow green:
And still I gaze—and with how blank an eye!
And those thin clouds above, in flakes and bars,
That give away their motion to the stars;
Those stars, that glide behind them or between,
Now sparkling, now bedimmed, but always seen:
Yon crescent Moon, as fixed as if it grew
In its own cloudless, starless lake of blue;
I see them all so excellently fair,
I see, not feel, how beautiful they are!

Coleridge, *Dejection: an Ode* C

A break in the clouds reveals a comet. Photo by David Levy of the comet he discovered in 1990.

Foreword

The heavens have captivated the curiosity, the imagination and the fears of life on earth throughout the eons of evolution. One can imagine the first form of life with the powers of observation being perplexed by magnificent cosmic displays. Think of the great herds of dinosaurs arching their heads skyward, perhaps pondering some magnificent change in the heavenly spectrum. Humanoids from their very beginning have marveled, feared, interpreted and used to advantage the wondrous changes of the sky. To gods of all sorts have been attributed the powers presumed to be lying in the firmament. Throughout it all the senses of humankind inspired and articulated the characteristics of curiosity, emotion, study, analysis, creativity—the continuum that evolved the arts and the sciences.

The magnetic pull of the heavens with their apparent infinite depth, the gentle twinkling of stars, the wonderful displays of "shooting stars," the appearance of the great comets, the milky way, the constellations and the planets, and the sound and the fury of electrical storms—all these things have played on the fears of the human race. Why are we here? Where did we come from? Give us a sign. The heavens have far too often complied with signs that have pointed to the best and the worst of human nature.

We have sought to explain these things. Artists have written, painted and brought through poetic expression all of the elements of the study of this vast unknown. Some of these artists have been called scientists as they pursued the stepwise analysis of the observations of the universal ether. The scientific method has added breadth to the great artistic pursuit of the unknown. Together, all of the curious have brought to us the detailed charts of the heavens, the travels of earth launched space craft, the awareness of black holes and red dwarfs, and still we are fascinated by the expanding mystery of the universe.

David Levy has pursued his dream. An earthbound explorer lifted into the heavens by the power of the telescope and by his own curiosity, David needed another critical human characteristic—the self confidence to make the mortal decision to gaze heavenly with the determination to look, to observe steadily and to record. Can anyone doubt the character required of a young man standing at his telescope, gazing at the heavens for an entire night through the clear skies offered on the Acadia campus? What must his fellow students have thought?

In the mold of scholars, artist-scientist Levy is now inscribed in those very heavens, traveling the orbit of twenty-one comets. With nature as artist, Maestro Levy commanded a worldwide orchestra as the most spectacular heavenly display ever recorded unfolded when Shoemaker-Levy 9 blended its more than twenty legions into the atmosphere of Jupiter with cosmic grace and fury. The pens of poets, philosophers, scribes and scientists move together to express the capacity of the human spirit lifted to the cosmos.

David Levy is a natural symbol of the oldest of truths, the continuum of artistic and scientific expression. From David's story let our universities learn again this essential truth. By lifting our spirits to such majestic heights perhaps he can help put back together on earth what mere mortals have torn asunder, the union of art and science.

Kelvin K. Ogilvie, C.M. Ph.D., D.Sc., F.C.I.C.
President of Acadia University

Introduction

Author's Convocation Address, Acadia University, 8 May 1995

May 8, 1995, is a day of hope. For the world, this is the fiftieth anniversary of V-E day, the end of World War II in Europe and a time to think optimistically about the future. What a privilege that you are graduating from Acadia on such a day. For your families looking at you with pride, this day brings the results of an investment—of money, of course, but also hope. How proud your families must feel that on this day, their hope comes to fruition.

I cannot begin to tell you how I feel being here with you today, receiving the great honor that Acadia is bestowing on me. Twenty-three years ago I stood here as you are, with a degree not in science but in arts. My parents were in the audience then. Mother, I'm glad to say, is in this audience today, but Father's chair is empty. For Dad in 1972, it was a special joy that I was getting an arts degree, because he saw poetry in so many things. I first realized that when I was eight years old. Dad showed me a special line in *Hamlet*: "There are more things in Heaven and Earth," Hamlet told his friend Horatio, "than are dreamt of in your philosophy." Not long after that, my interest turned to the sciences, upward to the sky, and then to comets and other worlds.

* * *

I entered Acadia in 1968 as a geology major. George Stevens taught Geology 100 at the time, and after three or four seconds in his first class, I felt that coming to Acadia had landed me in a pot of gold. Dr. Stevens evoked the wonder and the magic of Earth's geologic past, that Earth has a story written in page after page of rock. He also told me about Gene Shoemaker, a man who was studying the geology of other worlds.

Two years later I switched my major to English, and Roger Lewis introduced me to Tennyson's great 1850 poem *In Memoriam*. Tennyson was writing about the new science of evolution, and of the new world called Neptune. I thought I had made a polar academic switch, but here at Acadia, it was no switch at all! Science and poetry, I came to realize, were two parts of a single whole.

After her students, staff, alumni, and so much else, one of Acadia's greatest assets lies beyond the walls of classrooms and residences. This university is located where Nature is at its richest. From the roof of Crowell Tower, I could see it all—the highest tides on this planet surging in and out, and the night sky, which from here is among the finest in the world. On one night I spent almost ten hours with my eye at the eyepiece, moving the telescope slowly from field to field in the sky, searching for those small fuzzy worlds that we call comets. I also spent time listening to Roy Bishop of the Physics Department, and sharing my enthusiasm for the night sky. We talked a lot about comets those days. Comets are little worlds that orbit the Sun. They are 10 kilometer-wide snowballs that spend most of their time traveling in cold and silence at the edge of the solar system. It is only when they near the Sun that they grow and develop huge clouds of gas and dust as big as the whole Earth, and maybe even long tails that sweep grandly across the sky.

In 1989 I joined the husband-wife team of Gene and Carolyn Shoemaker, the same people I first heard about here at Acadia. Together we searched for comets and asteroids. On March 25, 1993, the Shoemakers and I found an extraordinary comet. Comets are named for their discoverers, and this comet was named Shoemaker-Levy 9. Acadia's mighty tides are no match for Jupiter's tidal yank on this comet, which disintegrated into 21 pieces. When we found the object, it looked like a string of pearls. Anyone who doubts that Jupiter could pull a comet apart should hike out to Cape Split where, thanks to the Moon's gravity, every few hours water surges into the Minas Basin with the force of all the rivers on Earth. I felt the power of Shoemaker-Levy 9 being torn apart by Jupiter when

I was at Cape Split four days ago. For one hour, ten to the twelfth gallons—a million million gallons—of water rushed by. For one hour, I heard the Moon roar. I could imagine the tidal power of Jupiter on that struggling little comet; naturally, the comet lost.

Shoemaker-Levy 9's tidal disruption, amazing as it turned out to be, was only its opening act. On July 16, 1994, the first of its pieces, racing along at 60 kilometers per second, slammed into Jupiter. By the end of what some call the most extraordinary week in the history of astronomy, all 21 pieces of the shattered comet had hit Jupiter with such force that fireballs rose more than three thousand kilometers above the planet, and the impacts left big, dark spots that even a child could see with a small telescope—huge dark clouds the size of the Earth. It was the most awe-inspiring event humanity had ever witnessed on another world. It was a marvelous display of Nature's power, reminding us what might have happened 65 million years ago when a comet striking Earth led to the extinction of the dinosaurs.

If Shoemaker-Levy 9 had struck the Earth instead, its pieces would have made craters 20 kilometers wide, and so much dust would have been thrown into the upper atmosphere that global temperatures would have plummeted. That means that Shoemaker-Levy 9's biggest impact was not felt on Jupiter at all, but right here on Earth. Jupiter and the comet taught us about our own environment, and how our biosphere has been shaped, and will be shaped again, by collisions with comets and asteroids. But more important, it provided us with a wonderful opportunity to get a whole generation excited about science. Comet Shoemaker-Levy 9 proved that science is not just for scientists. The comet showed that science is relevant, that it is in the here and now, and that it is worth our time and attention.

By watching a comet crash on a distant world, we could observe this portentous show of Nature in our neighbor's house, not our own. It was a culmination of what comet discoverer Leslie Peltier wrote in his autobiography, *Starlight Nights*:

> *Time has not lessened the age-old allure of the comets. In some ways their mystery has only deepened with the years. At each return a comet brings with it the questions which were asked when it was here before, and as it*

rounds the sun and backs away toward the long, slow night of its aphelion, it leaves behind with us those questions, still unanswered. To hunt a speck of moving haze may seem a strange pursuit, but even though we fail the search is still rewarding, for in no better way can we come face to face, night after night, with such a wealth of riches as old Croesus never dreamed of.[1]

In the scientific experience, the results we get are not as important as the process, the search. I followed a career in science, one that I prepared for by taking Acadia's courses in Geology and English Literature. Some of you have your careers all planned out, and others don't just yet. But you all have choices, and it is usually best to follow your own direction in life. Career decisions may not always appear logical, and they may even be wrong, but they need to be your own. It might be one of Acadia's greatest strengths that, because it is a small school in such beautiful natural surroundings, its graduates have been known to go off in unique paths.

Whatever your ultimate career, be a good teacher at it. Go into a classroom several times a year and tell the children why you have a passion for what you do. This plan will serve two purposes. You will get children excited about the field you're in, and each time you talk to kids you will be reminded of why you enjoy your work. It will keep the passion alive. You are being honored today with a Bachelor of Science degree, and with that honor comes a sense of *noblesse oblige*. By inspiring younger people in the path you have chosen, you will be fulfilling that obligation, and returning honour to Acadia, your alma mater.

* * *

Nature does what it wants, and so should you. Follow your heart and soul, as well as your head. And whatever you decide to do, be a good teacher at it. Finally, remember the poetry that there is in science.

For me, the poetry stretches all the way back to my first look at Jupiter through a small telescope. It was a beautiful clear night in Montreal, in the summer of 1960. I focused the telescope on the brightest star in the sky, which turned out to be mighty Jupiter, with its dark belts and four moons.

Watching me discover Jupiter that night brought my Dad back to his own

Comet Shoemaker-Levy 9, taken by Wieslaw Wiesniewski on March 28, 1993, just three days after discovery.

childhood. He told me about a novel he had read when he was a youngster. Titled *Cole of Spyglass Mountain*, the book was Arthur Preston Hankins's story about a boy whose love of the sky led him to observe Mars through his small homemade telescope. The novel ended when Cole found evidence of life on Mars one night and became an instant celebrity. "If you ever find that book," Dad said, "I'd like to read it again."

Five years later I began my long search for comets. As the years went by and Dad grew older, he would often ask if I had found *Cole of Spyglass Mountain*. Then he developed Alzheimer's disease, and his memory began to fail. As his time grew short we spent more of it together, and I watched helplessly as he forgot names, forgot people, and once even forgot that I was his son. But somehow he never forgot that electrifying story about a boy and a telescope.

When Comet Shoemaker-Levy 9 smashed into Jupiter, I felt as though I had rewritten *Cole of Spyglass Mountain* just for my father, and I will always regret that I could not share the most significant moment in my life with the most important person in it. Though Spyglass Mountain is fiction, it evokes the magic of discovering new things, whether these things are in the sky or in the pages of a book in some corner of a research library.

Dad, how I wish that you could have seen Shoemaker-Levy 9, and how I wish you could be here now. You could have helped me tell the world that this collision was about science, but it was, even more, about poetry. It was about following the dream I had on the roof of Crowell Tower here at Acadia. And Dad: more than anything, you were right about Hamlet: there are more things in Heaven and Earth than we can ever dream of.

How noteless Men, and Pleiads, stand,
Until a sudden sky
Reveals the fact that One is rapt
Forever from the Eye—

Members of the Invisible,
Existing, while we stare,
In Leagueless Opportunity,
O'ertakeless, as the Air—

Why didn't we detain Them?
The Heavens with a smile,
Sweep by our disappointed Heads
Without a syllable—

Emily Dickinson, c. 1891 Poem 282[D]

The Pleiades. Photo by Eugene and Carolyn Shoemaker and David Levy.

On a starred night Prince Lucifer uprose.
Tired of his dark dominion swung the fiend...
He reached a middle height, and at the stars,
Which are the brain of heaven, he looked, and sank.
Around the ancient track marched, rank on rank,
The army of unalterable law.

George Meredith, *Lucifer in Starlight* E

Two men look out through the same bars:
One sees the mud, and one the stars.

Frederick Langbridge,
A Cluster of Quiet Thoughts, 1896 F

The Pillars of Creation, showing a new star, with solar system, in formation. NASA/Hubble Space Telescope photograph.

Follow wise Orion
Till you waste your Eye—
Dazzlingly decamping
He is just as high—

Emily Dickinson
c. 1882, Poem 1538 [G]

You know Orion always comes up sideways,
Throwing a leg up over our fence of mountains,
And rising on his hands, he looks in on me
Busy outdoors by lantern-light with something
I should have done by daylight,...

Robert Frost, *The Star-Splitter* [H]

The Great Nebula in Orion.
Photograph by Rik Hill of
Tucson, Arizona.

Read Nature; Nature is a friend to truth...
Hast thou ne'er seen the comet's flaming flight?
The' illustrious stranger, passing, terror sheds
On gazing nations, from his fiery train
Of length enormous; takes his ample round
Through depths of ether; coasts unnumber'd worlds
Of more than solar glory; doubles wide
Heaven's mighty cape; and then revists earth,
From the long travel of a thousand years.
Thus, at the destined period, shall return...

Edward Young, *Night Thoughts*, 1741 [I]

Comet Hyakutake and a saguaro cactus plant.
Photo by David Levy.

*When the Astronomer stops seeking
For his Pleiad's Face—
When the lone British Lady
Forsakes the Arctic Race*

*When to his Covenant Needle
The Sailor doubting turns—
It will be amply early
To ask what treason means.*

Emily Dickinson, c. 1864, Poem 851 J

This Hubble Space Telescope Deep Space Image shows galaxies farther away than anything shown before. NASA image.

Till the sun grows cold,
And the stars are old,
And the leaves of the Judgement Book unfold!

Bayard Taylor, *Bedouin Song. Refrain* 1825-1878 [K]

Sky from Jarnac Pond. David Levy photo.

Opposite: The eastward-moving earth makes the stars circle the pole in this time exposure photograph by Rik Hill.

Move eastward, happy earth, and leave
Yon orange sunset waning slow;
From fringes of the faded eve,
O happy planet, eastward go,
Till over thy dark shoulder go
Thy silver sister-world, and rise
To glass herself in dewy eyes
That watch me from the glen below.
Ah, bear me with thee, smoothly borne,
Dip forward under starry light,
And move me to my marriage-morn,
And round again to happy night.

Alfred, Lord Tennyson
Move Eastward, Happy Earth, 1842 [M]

I am the owner of the sphere,
Of the seven stars and the solar year,
Of Caesar's hand, and Plato's brain,
Of Lord Christ's heart, and
Shakespeare's strain.

Ralph Waldo Emerson
The Informing Spirit [N]

The very source and fount of day
Is dash'd with wandering isles of night.

Tennyson, *In Memoriam,* 1850 [L]

Giant magnetic storms called sunspots march across the face of the Sun in this series of photographs by Leo Enright of Sharbot Lake, near Kingston, Ontario.

As lines, so loves oblique, may well
Themselves in every angle greet:
But ours, so truly parallel,
Though infinite, can never meet.

Therefore the love which us doth bind,
But Fate so enviously debars,
Is the conjunction of the mind,
And opposition of the stars.

The Aurora Borealis.
Photo by Leo Enright.

Andrew Marvell, *Definition of Love* [O]

Does this ageless sonnet evoke the vastness of this great and distant spiral galaxy? NGC 891 is an example of a galaxy viewed edge-on from Earth. Tim Hunter photo.

O deep of Heaven, 't is thou alone art boundless,
  'T is thou alone our balance shall not weigh,
'T is thou alone our fathom-line finds soundless,--
  Whose infinite our finite must obey!
Through thy blue realms and down thy starry reaches
  Thought voyages forth beyond the furthest fire,
And, homing from no sighted shoreline, teaches
  Thee measureless as in the soul's desire.
O deep of Heaven, no beam of Pleiad ranging
  Eternity may bridge thy gulf of spheres!
The ceaseless hum that fills thy sleep unchanging
  Is rain of the innumerable years.
Our worlds, our suns, our ages, these but stream
Through thine abiding like a dateless dream.

Sir Charles G.D. Roberts, *The Night Sky*, 1889 [P]

The Moon, photographed by David Levy.

**Above: Scorpius-Sagittarius Milky Way.
Roy Bishop photo.**

*I wandered lonely as a cloud
That floats on high o'er vales and hills,
When all at once I saw a crowd,
A host, of golden daffodils;
Beside the lake, beneath the trees,
Fluttering and dancing in the breeze.*

*Continuous as the stars that shine
And twinkle on the milky way,
They stretched in never-ending line
Along the margin of a bay:
Ten thousand saw I at a glance,
Tossing their heads in sprightly dance.*

William Wordsworth, *Daffodils*, 1807 Q

I will lift up mine eyes unto the mountains:
From whence cometh my help…

Psalm 121[R]

Twilight at Palomar Mountain Observatory. This view shows the dome of the two hundred-inch telescope taken through the open shutters of the 18-inch telescope dome. David Levy photo.

CHAPTER I

Choose Something Like a Star

Imagine a comet wandering through space like an ancient sailing ship. Rounding the Sun every few hundred thousand years, after a near miss with Jupiter, it changes its path and visits the Sun more frequently. Eventually its elliptical journey is shortened so greatly that it now orbits the Sun every 76 years. On one pass, a tiny particle of dust escapes. This particle travels on its own through space, rounding the Sun and occasionally dashing past Earth. Finally, one clear October night this particle, now racing along at some 60 kilometers per second, hurtles through the Earth's atmosphere. In a second it vaporizes to nothing, as an eight-year-old looks up and watches. After 4 1/2 billion years, the speck of dust gives its life to ignite a child's interest in the sky.

We have all seen shooting stars, which are not stars at all but the regions surrounding tiny particles that vaporize in the upper atmosphere of Earth. They look like falling stars, yet after one appears, the number of stars in the sky has not decreased. It is the bright flash of ionizing gases around the particle that we call a meteor. If the particle is larger, say the size of a tennis ball, it would hit Earth's atmosphere with a very bright streak. If it is as large as a basketball, it might survive its fall, leaving small pieces that hit the ground. These pieces are called meteorites.

In 1923, the American poet Robert Frost published a book of poems. Titled *New Hampshire*, the book included a poem about a small meteorite, a tiny remnant of a body in space, that ended up as part of a wall:

Never tell me that not one star of all
That slip from heaven at night and softly fall
Has been picked up with stones to build a wall.

Some laborer found one faded and stone cold...[2]

These lines beckon us into the intricate relationship among the sky, the Earth, and those who inhabit the Earth. We see a wall that stands as part of a house, or as part of a fence, or as the remains of the ancient Temple in Jerusalem—an artificial wall built with stones and bonding materials for some purpose. All of its stones, while ancient and enduring, have been gathered from some local quarry. But one stone in one wall is different. Traveling through space and hurtling to Earth, this rock, with so much to tell, has simply taken its place as one of many to hold up a wall, an ignominious end for such a noble stone.

Meteors are such simple parts of nature, and yet so wonderful, so mysterious; their beauty transcends their brevity, and they have captured the pens of earlier poets. In the 15th century John Donne began a song about explaining wonderful things:

Goe, and catche a falling starre,
Get with child a mandrake roote,
Tell me, where all past yeares are,
Or who cleft the Devil's foot.
Teach me to heare Mermaides singing,
Or to keep off envies stinging,
    And find
      What winde
Serves to advance an honest minde.[3]

Two hundred years later Byron pondered :

When the moon is on the wave,
And the glow-worm in the grass,
And the meteor on the grave,

And the wisp on the morass;
When the falling stars are shooting,
And the answer'd owls are hooting,
And the silent leaves are still
In the shadow of the hill
Shall my soul be upon thine,
With a power and with a sign.[4]

Although these references to meteors appear frivolous, they seem to share the notion that there is something momentous in the fall of matter from the sky, as Robert Southey wrote at the start of the 19th century in *St. Antidius, the Pope and the Devil* (circa 1800):

He ran against a shooting star,
So fast for fear did he sail,
And he singed the beard of the Bishop
Against a comet's tail;
And he passed between the horns of the moon,
With Antidius on his back;
And there was an eclipse that night,
Which was not in the almanac.[5]

In 1972 the American singer John Denver's song *Rocky Mountain High* immortalized a bright meteor spotted during a late night skywatch:

It's a Colorado Rocky Mountain high
I've seen it rainin' fire in the sky
Friends around the campfire and everybody's high
Rocky Mountain High.[6]

Rocky Mountain High, John Denver notes, was written after an observing session. "Imagine a moonless night in the Rockies in the dead of summer," Denver wrote. "I had insisted to everybody that it was going to be a glorious display. Spectacular, in fact.

"The air was kind of hazy when we started out, but by ten p.m. it had grown clear…I went back and lay down…when swoosh, a meteor went smoking by. And from all over the campground came the awed responses: 'Do you see that?' It got bigger and bigger until the tail stretched out all the way across the sky and burned itself out. Everybody was awake, and it was raining fire in the sky."[7]

Robert Frost was a part of this rich and varied tradition that sees a meteor as magic. To capture the image of the falling stone, Frost must have been well versed with the sky over New England, where on any night a hundred or more of these meteors would fall, most of them no heavier than a grain of sand. In rural New England, the nights are indeed dark and beautiful, unlike city nights, where fear and suspicion rule over beauty.

It is over all these kinds of nights that Frost seemed to preside when, in 1928, he published *Acquainted with the Night*:

> *I have been one acquainted with the night.*
> *I have walked out in rain—and back in rain.*
> *I have outwalked the furthest city light.*
>
> *I have looked down the saddest city lane.*
> *I have passed by the watchman on his beat*
> *And dropped my eyes, unwilling to explain.*
>
> *I have stood still and stopped the sound of feet*
> *When far away an interrupted cry*
> *Came over houses from another street,*
>
> *But not to call me back or say good-by;*
> *And further still at an unearthly height,*
> *One luminary clock against the sky*
>
> *Proclaimed the time was neither wrong nor right.*
> *I have been one acquainted with the night.*[8]

Although this exquisite poem addresses all of the night, the fear as well as the wonder, its opening line is a skygazer's mantra. The poem's message is about the magic of night, the clarity that comes from the rain, and the warmth that comes from its cold, and finally the sparkling clarity of a sky that is dark and filled with stars. Many poets have allowed rich images of the sky to permeate their poetry. But as the richness of the night sky has appeared in poem after poem, it is the purpose of this chapter to explore how some poets—not just Frost—took advantage of the majesty that lies above us each clear night.

A clear, dark night is one of nature's most precious gifts, a chance to be as one with the Universe. My own direct experience with several of the images of this poem began on a warm August night in the middle 1960s, when I did drop my eyes, "unwilling to explain," as a police car pulled up to my parents' home at 4:00 in the morning. Jupiter had just risen in the east, and I pointed my telescope toward it in order to draw its features. The planet had barely cleared the roof of my neighbor's house when the police arrived. As they stepped onto the walk, I was certain that they would accuse me of spying on the neighbors. They drew closer and closer, and stopped, military style, right next to my telescope. "Excuse me, sir," one of the officers quipped, "would you mind if a couple of nosy policemen looked at Jupiter?"

On many nights I have walked out in rain, past the furthest city light, in a usually vain hope of observing a lunar eclipse or some other astronomical event. On one of these occasions, in 1985, I hoped to obtain an electronic image of Halley's comet, which was approaching our part of the solar system for the first time since 1910. I arrived at the observatory and waited for more than an hour while the driving rain echoed so loudly on the dome that I couldn't hear anything else. But then the sound faded, the rain stopped, and there appeared a small hole in the clouds. Setting the telescope up at Halley's proper coordinates for that night, I left the dripping observatory dome tightly shut. Meantime, the small clear area was moving closer to where the comet was. When the comet finally became visible, I quickly opened the dome and took a two-minute exposure of the famous visitor. The wait was worth it, for I had surreptitiously captured Halley's first major outburst of a jet of dust in more than 75 years. When I left the observatory that night, the clouds had taken over once again; I did indeed walk back in rain.

AN ANCIENT LUMINARY CLOCK

The luminary clock against the sky, proclaiming the time as neither wrong nor right, is one of my favorite images, a picture often conjured in English poetry. Here it appears in Coleridge's *Rime of the Ancient Mariner*:

> *The moving Moon went up the sky,*
> *And no where did abide:*
> *Softly she was going up,*
> *And a star or two beside—* [9]

Although most of us never realize it, the Moon does keep its own time, rising 30 minutes to an hour later each night. On fully half the nights of the month, the Moon either rises so early that it is visible during the afternoon, or so late that it stays in the sky until late in the morning. Hopkins noted this in his 1862 piece *A fragment of anything you like*:

> *Fair, but of fairness as a vision dream'd;*
> *Dry were her sad eyes that would fain have stream'd;*
> *She stood before a light not hers, and seem'd*
>
> *The lorn Moon, pale with piteous dismay,*
> *Who rising late had miss'd her painful way*
> *In wandering until broad light of day;*
>
> *Then was discover'd in the pathless sky,*
> *White-faced, as one in sad assay to fly*
> *Who asks not life but only place to die.* [10]

The appearance of the Moon—not just its timing, but its shape, and its effect on clouds and landscape—has also long been a poetic choice. Whether the Moon is in the sky at night is a question that interests poets as well as astronomers. A moonlit night welcomes peaceful evening walks that are less inviting when the night sky is dark. However, it is only during the four days nearest full Moon when moonlight makes a very noticeable difference—only 21/2 days before full Moon the sky is only half as bright. Thomas Gray, whose words are capable of turning a simple scene of a darkening sky into one of the most heart-felt images in the English language, is also skillful at turning the absence of moonlight into a profound sense of loss. This passage comes from a journal Gray kept of a tour through English Lakes: *At distance heard the murmur of many waterfalls not audible in the day-time. Wish'd for the Moon, but she was dark to me & silent, hid in her vacant interlunar cave.*[11]

When the Moon shines through high cirrus clouds, it often surrounds itself with a halo of light.

Samuel Taylor Coleridge wrote of

The Moon, rushing onward through the coursing clouds, advances like an indignant warrior through a fleeing army; but the amber halo in which he moves—O! It is a circle of Hope. For what she leaves behind her has not lost its radiance as it is melting away into oblivion, while, still, the other semicircle catches the rich light at her approach, and heralds her ongress.[12]

Gerard Manley Hopkins wrote often of haloes, like this lunar one of February 1872:

The halo was not quite round, for in the first place it was a little pulled and drawn below, by the refraction of the lower air perhaps, but what is more it fell in on the nether left hand side to rhyme the moon itself, which was not quite at full. I could not but strongly feel in my fancy the odd instress of this, the moon leaning on her side, as if fallen back, in the cheerful light floor within the ring, after with magical rightness and success tracing round her the ring the steady copy of her own outline.[13]

Whenever the Moon's phase is thin enough, we can see the dark part as well as the bright. This effect, called earthshine, results from the Earth's shining on the Moon's dark side. Anyone standing on the dark part of the Moon at such a time would have a sky brightly lit by the Earth. Here at home, earthshine is not to be feared, notwithstanding the poor sailor in the ballad of *Sir Patrick Spens*:

Late, late yestreen I saw the new moone
      Wi' the auld moone in her arme;
And I feir, I feir, my deir master,
      That we will com to harm.[14]

Nor can a star appear within the dark section of the Moon, notwithstanding this bad omen from Coleridge's *Ancient Mariner.*

We listened and looked sideways up!
Fear at my heart, as at a cup,
My lifeblood seemed to sip!
The stars were dim, and thick the night,
The steersman's face by his lamp gleamed white:
From the sails the dew did drip—
Till clomb above the eastern bar
The hornèd moon, with one bright star
Within the nether tip.[15]

The Moon has an aspect that is beyond time, though, or at least beyond the length of time we can imagine: the story of its cratered surface we see through binoculars or a telescope. While here on Earth we live in areas that are surrounded by local rocks of a certain age, a single look at the Moon gives the whole panorama of its 4.5 billion year history. The Moon was probably created as the result of a shotgun marriage between two great worlds, the Earth and another large body with which it collided more than four billion years ago. So violent was the crash that the Earth's crust melted away, and a storm of rocky material from the Earth and the other world formed a thick ring around the Earth. Eventually that material congealed to form the Moon. And if the Moon was born in violence, it has lived its life that way too. Even without a telescope or binoculars, anyone can see the large grey areas that form the face of what some call "the man in the Moon." Some of these are impact basins, formed when objects struck the Moon in an ancient blitz that took place some 3.9 billion years ago. Much later these basins filled with dark basalt, a lava that gives them their dark appearance. Finally, through a telescope, one can see hundreds of small craters, all formed when asteroids or comets struck the Moon throughout its history. One of the youngest major craters on the Moon, Tycho, was formed when a comet or an asteroid struck the Moon some 100 million years ago. When the Moon is near its full phase, one can see the rays of rocky material that shot out from the center of that impact site, marking this relatively recent change in the Moon's long history.

> *Think'st thou I'd make a life of jealousy;*
> *To follow still the changes of the moon*
> *With fresh suspicions? No; to be once in doubt*
> *Is once to be resolved.*[16]

THESE LATE ECLIPSES OF THE SUN AND MOON

When the Earth, Moon, and Sun line up perfectly, the shadow of one falls on another and an eclipse occurs. When the Moon is positioned directly between the Earth and Sun, its shadow falls on a small portion of the Earth; the result is a solar eclipse. A lunar eclipse occurs when the Earth travels between the Sun and the Moon; the darkening of the Moon is the effect of the Moon's passing directly through the Earth's shadow. Made to extract feelings of wonder, eclipses are not everyday events. Not only was Shakespeare well aware of the beauty and power of an eclipse, but also he understood the debate over the role that these events play in our lives. In *King Lear* he constructed the famous argument between the Earl of Gloucester and Edmund, his bastard son, about whether an astronomical event can portend evil for humanity. In Edmund's opening appearance he announces his commitment to rational thinking: *"Thou, Nature, art my goddess; to thy Law/ My services are bound."* But in a speech permeated with concern for the future, the Earl of Gloucester argues: *"These late eclipses of the sun and moon portend no good to us. Though the wisdom of nature can reason it thus and thus, yet nature finds itself scourged by the sequent effects. Love cools, friendship falls off, brothers divide."*[17]

Not so, counters Edmund, who fires back: *"This is the excellent foppery of the world, that when we are sick in fortune, often the surfeits of our own behavior, we make guilty of our disasters the sun, the moon, and stars; as if we were villains on necessity…"*[18]

Anyone who has experienced the grandeur of an eclipse, be it of the Sun or the Moon, understands the poetic inspiration that it provokes. Eclipses are profound events, in no small part because their four-body lineup is one in which we participate—Sun, Moon, Earth, and observer. In a sense, we observers are not unlike the meteor that ended up in a wall in Frost's poem quoted earlier in this chapter. But the drama of an eclipse is far easier to appreciate. In July 1991, I watched a magnificent total solar eclipse from Mexico's Baja California peninsula.

The sky did not darken linearly and steadily, as it does after sunset. For the first half hour, the bright summer sky made it hard to imagine that anything unusual was happening at all. My first thought that the light was changing came as I noticed that the sky was not quite as bright as it should be for a summer desert near noon. Through my welder's glass I looked and saw that fully half the Sun was gone. By the time the Sun was three-quarters covered, the pace of darkening was increasing rapidly. Now navy blue, the sky was darkening as fast as if someone were operating a dimmer switch. Soon there was just a sliver of Sun left, and I could see

the Sun shrink as the seconds ticked away. Directly to the west the dark shadow of the Moon gained substance. The scene ripped to the core of my being; something inside wanted to hold it back for a few minutes so that I could find a key and lock this moment. But still the sky grew darker.

When I looked again, the Sun had gone. In its place was a golden crown stretching some three solar diameters east and west;

The total eclipse of the Sun, 26 February, 1969. Photo by David Levy.

through the telescope this garland was rich with streamers and intricate brushes of light. On the north and south sides were a series of smaller eruptions of rays, shining outward like the mouths of baby birds in a nest. Eclipses heighten the senses: listening to the sounds of the eclipse—the birds flying and strutting about, the incessant clicks of a million cameras—all accompanied the eerie light that surrounded us. Around the horizon was a bright red glow. In the final seconds of totality the western sky started to brighten rapidly. I looked back at the Sun, admiring a red tongue of flame, or prominence, as the western edge brightened quickly. Suddenly a sharp speck of photosphere stabbed the darkness, then slowly spread out into a thin crescent. The eclipse was over, yet it wasn't over. As the Moon crept away, it left an ever larger crescent Sun, a rapidly brightening landscape, and a euphoric crowd of people.

The Bard wrote again about an eclipse in Sonnet 107:

> *The mortal moon hath her eclipse endur'd;*
> *And the sad augurs mock their own presage.*[19]

Milton also understood the strong, basic feelings that solar eclipses generate. He wrote of solar eclipses in *Samson Agonistes*:

> *O dark, dark, dark, amid the blaze of noon,*
> *Irrecoverably dark, total eclipse,*
> *Without all hope of day!*[20]

In *Paradise Lost*, he wrote:

> *The sun...*
> *In dim eclipse disastrous twilight shreds*
> *On half the nations, and with fear of change*
> *Perplexes monarchs.*[21]

Some three centuries after *Paradise Lost*, the great novelist Thomas Hardy was inspired to write as Milton did about shadows and nations. But Hardy's eclipse was of the Moon, not the Sun, and while a lunar eclipse lacks the drama of a solar eclipse, it offers its own special majesty to anyone who views it. To see a coppery red Moon in the sky offers a feeling of serenity more than of drama. *At a Lunar Eclipse*, written in 1903, is a song to the Earth, whose shadow was reflected upon the Moon:

> *Thy shadow, Earth, from Pole to Central Sea*
> *Now steals along upon the Moon's meek shine*
> *In even monochrome and curving line*
> *Of imperturbable serenity.*

How shall I like such sun-cast symmetry
With the torn troubled form I know as thine,
That profile, placid as a brow divine,
With continents of moil and misery?

And can immense mortality but throw
So small a shade, and Heaven's high human scheme
Be hemmed within the coasts yon arc implies?

Is such a stellar gauge of earthly show,
Nation at war with nation, brains that teem,
Heroes, and women fairer than the skies?[22]

THE MAGIC OF NIGHT

We have already seen John Keats's exultant feeling of discovery after reading Chapman's Homer with his friend, but we should read also his mournful calling, in his last years, to a lone bright star:

Bright star, would I were stedfast as thou art—
        Not in lone splendor hung aloft the night
And watching, with eternal lids apart,
        Like nature's patient, sleepless Eremite,
The moving waters at their priestlike task
        Of pure ablution round earth's human shores,
Or gazing on the new soft fallen mask
        Of snow upon the mountains and the moors—
No—yet still stedfast, still unchangeable,
        Pillowed upon my fair love's ripening breast,
To feel forever its soft fall and swell,
        Awake forever in a sweet unrest,
Still still to hear her tender-taken breath,
And so live ever—or else swoon to death.[23]

In modern times, Stephen Crane posed a similar philosophical query, and emerged with a very different result:

> *A man said to the universe,*
> *"Sir, I exist!"*
> *"However," replied the universe,*
> *"The fact has not created in me*
> *A sense of obligation."*[24]

The poem offers an intriguing paradox, with the insignificant human posing the mother of all statements—that of existence— to the Universe. Obviously the Universe doesn't care, but the fact that it answers the man's query at all both completes the poem and, in a sense, invalidates its theme.

Not so, wrote Max Ehrmann in 1948's *Desiderata*: *"You are a child of the universe, no less than the trees and the stars, you have a right to be here. And whether or not it is clear to you, no doubt the universe is unfolding as it should."*[25]

We return now to Robert Frost, who frequently wrote of night in his poems. The sky appeared early in Frost's life; at age 16 he sold subscriptions to a magazine called *The Youth's Companion*. Using star maps from the local library in Lawrence, Massachusetts, he used his telescope to find and study the sky's wealth of diverse objects. In 1912 his first book of poems, *A Boy's Will*, included this early sign of his consciousness of the night sky:

> *How countlessly they congregate*
> *· O'er our tumultuous snow,*
> *Which flows in shapes as tall as trees*
> *When wintry winds do blow!—*
>
> *As if with keenness for our fate,*
> *Our faltering few steps on*
> *To white rest, and a place of rest*
> *Invisible at dawn,—*
>
> *And yet with neither love nor hate,*

Those stars like some snow-white
Minerva's snow-white marble eyes
Without the gift of sight.[26]

Frost continued to indulge his interest in nature. After entering Harvard in 1897, he studied both arts and science, including a course in historical geology. When he dropped out of Harvard at age 25, his grandfather gave him a farm in

Derry, New Hampshire, on condition that he run it for ten years. Although he was not much more successful as a farmer than he was at Harvard, something about the land and the sky touched his soul. After a stay in England he settled in New Hampshire and Vermont.

By 1921, Frost was in considerable demand to give poetry readings and lectures; he even spent a week as poet in residence at Queen's University in Kingston, Canada.[27] He was fusing his love of nature with a career as a poet of nature. In his 1936 collection, *A Further Range*, he published these lines:

Robert Frost

My object in living is to unite
My avocation and my vocation
As my two eyes make one in sight.
Only where love and need are one,
And the work is play for mortal stakes,
Is the deed ever really done
For Heaven and the future's sakes.[28]

In 1947 Frost wrote this dedication to the human dream that it is good for the mind to set lofty goals, and to work to achieve them:

O Star (the fairest one in sight),
We grant your loftiness the right
To some obscurity of cloud—
. . .

Not even stooping from its sphere,
It asks a little of us here.
It asks of us a certain height,
So when at times the mob is swayed
To carry praise or blame too far,
We may choose something like a star
To stay our minds on and be staid.[29]

It is also human nature to enjoy the less starry events of life, as Frost writes:

Lord, I have loved your sky,
Be it said against or for me,
Have loved it clear and high,
Or low and stormy;

Till I have reeled and stumbled
From looking up too much,
And fallen and been humbled
To wear a crutch.[30]

One spring evening in 1996, I was observing Comet Hyakutake from the front steps of my friend Tim Hunter's house. Since its discovery a few weeks earlier, the comet had been brightening fast. I enjoyed watching it from odd locations like the window of a moving train, or the yard of a school filled with enthusiastic children. On that Friday night, the comet was rising early enough to be conspicuous in the evening sky—already as bright as Comet Levy, one of my own comets, was six years earlier—its show, I knew, was only beginning. I watched as the comet, now a bright fluffy object in the southeast, rose over my friend's roof.

I stood transfixed at the sight, but I should have had one eye on the ground. As I took one step to get a better view, I lost my balance. I fell down Tim's front steps, sprained my left ankle, and damaged a nerve in my right arm. I lay there in too much pain to think of Charles Messier, the world's first serious comet hunter, who had a far more serious accident some two hundred years ago. With his close friend Jean Baptiste de Saron, then President of the Paris Parliament, Messier was visiting an oriental garden at the Parc Monceau, a place with many small pago-das, castles and passageways. Somehow Messier got separated from de Saron, and he saw a small open door. Curious as always, he stepped through. There was noth-ing inside but a long drop to a storeroom of ice. Before he could regain his bal-ance, Messier fell twenty-five feet, cutting his scalp and breaking an arm, a leg, and several ribs as he crashed onto the ice below. In hospital and then at home, Messier was away from his telescope for almost a year.

I think both poet Frost and scientist Messier would have enjoyed my rare view of a bright comet near the pole that March night. For as the comet contin-ued to brighten, it headed northward along one of the most famous highways of the sky—the curved line that joins Spica and Arcturus with the Dipper's handle. On Friday, March 22, 1996, I observed the moon-sized comet head near Arcturus, with the naked eye from a parking lot of a Denny's restaurant in a Chicago sub-urb. As the comet closed in on Ursa Major and Polaris, it did something that no major comet apparition can boast of—it brightened to brighter than zero magni-tude, grew a mighty tail, and stayed in the northern sky from dusk until dawn.

In 1855, Robert Browning wrote these words in *Andrea del Sarto*:

> *Ah, but a man's reach should exceed his grasp,*
> *Or what's a heaven for?*

When a bright comet splashes its way across the sky, or an eclipse brings darkness at noon, we look toward the heavens with a sense of wonder. These events are magical, their "imperturbable serenity" inspiring us to rise above who we are. Further, they link us to times long past, when mankind first looked up in wonder as a meteor fell from the sky.

CHAPTER II

Stars,
Hide Your Fires

The Universe is a most fertile subject for poetry, and considering the importance of the sky to early watchers, it is not surprising to find astronomical references even in ancient literature. The first book of *Chronicles* describes what could be a comet—the comet of 971 BC appeared near that time—which signaled God's protest of an ill-advised census King David had ordered. The biblical passage is read every year at the Passover seder: *And David lifted up his eyes, and saw the angel of the Lord standing between the earth and the heaven, having a drawn sword in his hand stretched out over Jerusalem.*[31]

Around 760 BC, the prophet Amos wrote of what could have been the solar eclipse of 762 BC in Nineveh:

> *And it shall come to pass in that day,*
> *Saith the Lord God,*
> *That I will cause the sun to go down at noon*
> *And I will darken the earth in the clear day.*[32]

In *Isaiah* there is a strange passage that may refer to a large partial solar eclipse over Jerusalem on January 11, 688 BC:

> *Behold, I will cause the shadow of the dial, which is gone down on the*

sun-dial of Ahaz, to return backward ten degrees. So the sun returned ten degrees, by which degrees it was gone down.[33]

MEDIEVAL ENGLISH LITERATURE BEFORE THE NEW PHILOSOPHY

In the fourteenth century, Geoffrey Chaucer's *Treatise on the Astrolabe* was a rare literary work which explained the workings of the major astronomical instrument of the time, the astrolabe. This was as surprising a production as if the most famous poet of our age should write a treatise about modern astronomical telescopes. It is possible that Chaucer took a much dimmer view of using the stars to predict one's future than he did of their scientific value. In *The Miller's Tale*, one of the most humorous of *The Canterbury Tales*, Geoffrey Chaucer pokes fun at the astrologer who walks into a field to gaze at the stars to discern what they predict, and falls into a pit:

> *So ferde another clerk with astromye;*
> *He walked into the feeldes, for to prye*
> *Upon the sterres, what ther sholde bifalle,*
> *Til he was in a marle-pit yfalle:*
> *He saugh nat that.*[34]

Of all the objects in the sky, the temporary ones—the exploding stars or novae—and the moving ones—the comets—obviously attracted the most attention in ancient times. Rarely a supernova would blast forth, a star whose core collapses in a titanic explosion. In historic times one appeared in 1054, a second in 1572, and a third in 1604. Of the moving objects, comets flew in and then moved away, bringing with them a xenophobic fear of the unknown.

In *Julius Caesar*, Shakespeare writes of Calpurnia, who, having dreamt of an apparition in the sky, begged her husband Julius Caesar not to travel to the Senate: "When beggars die," Calpurnia exclaimed, "there are no comets seen. The heavens themselves blaze forth the death of princes."[35]

Caesar ignored her pleas, left for the Senate anyway, and was assassinated as he sat under Pompeii's statue. "Et tu, Brute!" he moaned as he saw his friend

Brutus leading the plot, "Then fall, Caesar!"

Calpurnia might have been right about the comet, but the historical record tells us that she could not have seen one before her husband was killed. During the Octavian games held a few weeks after his death, a bright comet moved slowly from night to night in the northern sky. The comet was widely interpreted as Caesar's soul traveling to the stars.

MORE THINGS IN HEAVEN AND EARTH: ASTROLOGICAL MYTH AND SCIENCE IN SHAKESPEARE

Shakespeare's most active period coincided with a number of unusual events, especially the suggestion by Nicholas Copernicus as far back as 1543 that the Earth was not the center of the universe. However, when Shakespeare was writing his greatest plays, the real impact of Copernicus's ideas had yet to be felt. Cosmic events were happening, but slowly. There was a supernova in 1572; the great astronomer Tycho Brahe interpreted it as meaning that the sphere of fixed stars that lay beyond the planets might not be so unchangeable as people had thought. Five years later, a bright comet led Tycho to suggest that comets were not a part of the atmosphere (a view that had dominated cometary science since Aristotle first suggested it) and that they moved methodically in a sphere beyond the Moon. Queen Elizabeth herself defied royal tradition not to set eyes on transient events in the sky by observing the comet of 1582, and a second supernova appeared in 1604.

Tycho's ideas were based on meticulous observation, rather than the theoretical arguments that led philosophers to accept the *Almagest* of Ptolemy, a work that championed the Earth-centered Universe and which was considered as virtual gospel since its appearance around 150 AD. Far in advance of his time, Tycho's idea of basing arguments on observation would not gain support until 1620, when Francis Bacon published *Novum Organum* (see next chapter).

Shakespeare's references to the sky are rich in the casual astrology of the time, as when, for example, the two characters Helena and Parolles trade views on their astrological predicaments:

Helena: *Monsieur Parolles, you were born under a charitable star.*
Parolles: *Under Mars, I.*
Helena: *I especially think, under Mars.*
Parolles: *Why under Mars?*
Helena: *The wars hath kept you under that you must needs be born under Mars.*
Parolles: *When he was predominant.*
Helena: *When he was retrograde, I think, rather.*
Parolles: *Why think you so?*
Helena: *You go so much backward when you fight.*
Parolles: *That's for advantage.*
Helena: *So is running away, when fear proposes the safety; but the composition that your valour and fear makes in you is a virtue of a good wing, and I like the wear well.*[36]

Had Shakespeare's prime writing years ended a decade later, his plays might have reflected a vastly different situation. After Galileo's crucial observations of Jupiter, Venus, the Moon, and the Sun, philosophers and writers had to contend with the mounting evidence for the new philosophy of a universe in which the Earth circles the Sun rather than one in which the Sun orbits the Earth. References to the Sun-centered universe in writing before 1610 are rare, but after that critical year they become more common. Shakespeare, according to the well-known critic Marjorie Hope Nicholson, "lived in a world of Time, Milton in a universe of Space. It happened as suddenly as that."[37]

In chapter one we explored Gloucester's speech about the "late eclipses" of both Sun and Moon. These eclipses were actually used to help date the play, but two eclipses in 1605 that are most commonly cited may not have been the ones Shakespeare had in mind. Johnstone Parr, among other critics, wondered which of the three solar eclipses that occurred around the writing of *Lear*, or whether all had been planted in Gloucester's thoughts. But the historical record shows that England was free of any major solar eclipse for more than half a century, a most unusually long period that lasted from 1547 to 1598. Then three major eclipses of the Sun tracked close to England in rapid succession. The central line of the annular eclipse of 1601, in fact, passed near London. In such an eclipse, the

Moon is too far from Earth to cover the Sun completely as it passes in front of it, so that viewers on the central line would see an annulus, or ring, of sunlight surrounding the darkened Moon.

Shakespeare may well have had the September 27, 1605, eclipse of the Sun, as well as the lunar eclipse that preceded it by two weeks, in mind when he wrote Gloucester's words in *Lear*. But the solar eclipse was a small one that would not have created great excitement. More likely, Shakespeare intended a general reference to the sudden occurrence of several eclipses.[38] There are other references to eclipses such as the poignant one in *Antony and Cleopatra*, where Anthony fears:

> *Alack, our terrene moon*
> *Is now eclips'd, and it portends alone*
> *The fall of Antony.*[39]

These references are to astronomical events, which would have interested Shakespeare's audiences more than arcane discussions of astronomical theory would. In fact, we find very few Shakespearean references to Copernicus and his ideas. Hamlet's love letter to Ophelia, however, is an exception:

> *Doubt thou the stars are fire,*
> *Doubt that the sun doth move,*
> *Doubt truth to be a liar,*
> *But never doubt I love.*[40]

Although there are several versions of *Hamlet*, the line "doubt that the sun doth move" does appear in the first good text of the play, the Second Quarto published around 1604 or 1605. This was more than half a decade before Galileo's observations. Even if Shakespeare had believed in the new cosmology, it would not have served his purpose well, for the old system, with its emphasis on the Earth and mankind at the center of the universe, is more sound for the purpose of drama. After all, why would the heavens have blazed forth the death of princes in Calpurnia's dream, if the princes had not been at the center of the universe?

What is interesting is not which set of cosmic rules concerned Shakespeare but that he did have a lively interest in the sky. This interest is obvious in the 135 references in the canon to stars, 19 to planets, 11 to eclipses, and 7 to comets,[41] not to mention the 800 less specific invocations to heaven of which the most famous is probably Hamlet's cry to his friend:

> *There are more things in heaven and earth, Horatio,*
> *Than are dreamt of in your philosophy.*

Besides this listing is the fact, noted by critic Wolfgang Clemen, that almost every major tragic hero in Shakespeare must contend with the forces of the cosmos, a trait not matched by heroes in the histories or the comedies:

> When in the histories, the people turned their eyes to the sun, taking its dull gleam for a foreboding of evil, this was in the tradition of omen. But in the tragedies, the characters apostrophize the sun and stars directly. "Stars, hide your fires,…" (I: iv, 50) Macbeth cries before his murderous deed. "Moon and stars!" we hear Antony say, and Cleopatra: "O Sun, burn the great sphere…". The heavens seem sympathetic to what is occurring here on earth. To Hamlet, thinking of his mother's hasty remarriage, "heaven's face doth glow" (III: iv, 48) and Othello, convinced of Desdemona's faithlessness, cries out: "Heaven stops the nose at it and the moon winks" (IV: ii, 77). Moreover, in the dramatic structure of the individual tragedies the appeal to the elements makes its appearance at definite turning-points. Not until they begin to despair of men and earth do the tragic heroes turn to the heavens. When their firmest beliefs have been shaken, when they stand alone and forsaken, they renounce the earth and call upon the cosmic powers.[42]

The single concept that all these apostrophes have in common is not a fear of but a respect for the power of the cosmos. In Renaissance England the cosmic debate involved two separate but related ideas, both called astrology. There was the natural astrology, which considered the planetary motions and the positions of other celestial objects in their spheres, and the judicial astrology, which concerned itself with the effects of these motions on humans. The modern term "astronomy" was, in Elizabethan times, used as a synonym for either branch of astrology, as Edgar shows us in *Lear*:

> Edmund: *I am thinking, brother, of a prediction I read the other day what should follow these eclipses.*
>
> Edgar: *Do you busy yourself with that?...*
> *How long have you been a sectary astronomical?*[43]

There is considerable debate as to how seriously many Elizabethans followed or believed in the ideas and predictions of the judicial astrologers. Critic J.W. Draper suggests that the people were committed to these ideas, and that Queen Elizabeth regularly employed the learned Dr. John Dee to compute for her the lucky days and hours for conducting her affairs.[44] However, Elizabeth defied her own council by observing the Great Comet of 1582, and Dr. Dee was known as a Copernican astrologer whose advice was received more for its informative value than for its predictive power. In any event, at the time, there was considerable religious opposition to judicial astrology, since its practice violated the first commandment. According to Warren D. Smith, the fact that Elizabeth's second parliament passed the first of a series of anti-judicial astrology bills, each harsher than the last, indicates that people did practice astrology and that other people objected to its practice. The Act of 1580, in fact, compared judicial astrology to witchcraft and threatened the death penalty for the practice of either. James I also disdained the practice, distinguishing between astronomia, the law of the stars, and astrologia, the preaching of the stars. Of the latter James wrote: "It is this part which I called before the devils schole."[45]

"...to hitch his wagon to a star."

Emerson
Society and Solitude: Civilization[5]

Astronomy might have been practiced in observatories like this one. England's Stonehenge is a towering and magnificent place. The ruins of what was probably an observatory and temple, Stonehenge has a long and glorious history. Beginning as a simple ditch and circle of 56 pits dug around 3100 BC, the structure was expanded, rebuilt, and rebuilt again over more than two thousand years. David Levy photo.

If Elizabethans, or at least their government, scoffed at the judicial astrologers, they certainly enjoyed hearing from them throughout Shakespeare's plays. We do not have to look far to find evidence that Shakespeare capitalized on this popular interest from his earliest plays to his last. In *The Two Gentlemen of Verona*, Julia speaks of her love for Proteus:

> *Base men, that use them to so base effect!*
> *But truer stars did govern Proteus' birth;*
> *His words are bonds...*[46]

We have already seen Helena praise Parolles' "charitable star" in *All's Well That Ends Well*. It appears that Shakespeare was familiar with astrological concepts, and used them effectively. *Richard II*, for example, offers a far more serious invocation to the cosmos' judicial power:

> Captain: *'Tis thought the king is dead; we will not stay.*
> *The bay-trees in our country are all wither'd*
> *And meteors fright the fixed stars of heaven;*
> *The pale-faced moon looks bloody on the earth*
> *And lean-look'd prophets whisper fearful change ...*[47]

Hamlet's Horatio recalls a scene from *Julius Caesar*, then adds more to it:

> *...A little ere the mightiest Julius fell,*
> *The graves stood tenantless and the sheeted dead*
> *Did squeak and gibber in the Roman streets;*
> *As stars with trains of fire and dews of blood,*
> *Disasters in the sun; and the moist star*
> *Upon whose influence Neptune's empire stands*
> *Was sick almost to doomsday with eclipse...*[48]

Henry VIII, probably Shakespeare's last play, returns to the image of the falling star in *Richard II*. During the coronation scene two gentlemen converse:

Second Gentleman: *Those men are happy, and so are all are near her.*
I take it, she that carries up the train
Is that old noble lady, Duchess of Norfolk.
First Gentleman: *It is; and all the rest are countesses.*
Second Gentleman: *Their coronets say so. These are stars indeed;*
And sometimes falling ones.
First Gentleman: *No more of that.*[49]

This is a sample of the plethora of astrological references in Shakespeare's writing. Of the 135 references to stars in the canon, 47 directly invoke the power of judicial astrology. Shakespeare expresses a particular interest in the Pleiades. In *1 Henry IV* Falstaff says:

> *Indeed, you come near me now, Hal; for we that take purses go by the moon and the seven stars, and not by Phœbus, he, 'that wandering knight so fair.*[50]

In *2 Henry IV* Pistol excitedly announces to Falstaff that "we have seen the seven stars."[51] And *Lear*'s Fool suggests:

> *Thy asses are gone about 'em. The reason why the seven stars are no more than seven is a pretty reason.*
> Lear: *Because they are not eight?*
> Fool: *Yes, indeed: thou wouldst make a good fool.*[52]

Does Shakespeare deliberately exploit judicial astrology just for dramatic impact, and does he not really believe in it? From Edmund's answer to his father's fear of the "late eclipses" (see chapter one) it would seem that Shakespeare is certainly aware of the argument against judicial astrology. There are other brilliant references, such as Cassius's plea to Brutus in *Julius Caesar*:

> *Men at some time are masters of their fates;*
> *The fault, dear Brutus, is not in our stars,*
> *But in ourselves, that we are underlings.*[53]

But then we have *Macbeth*, who thinks he can command the stars, rather than being commanded by them:

> *Stars, hide your fires,*
> *Let not light see my black and deep desires.*[54]

It turned out that Macbeth had power over the stars after all, as Banquo later reports:

> *There's husbandry in heaven;*
> *Their candles are all out.*[55]

Shakespeare occasionally invokes the north celestial pole to show strength of character. The most famous such reference, of course, is Caesar's:

> *But I am constant as the northern star*
> *Of whose true-fix'd and resting quality*
> *There is no fellow in the firmament.*[56]

In *Lear*, Edmund claims that his "nativity was under Ursa Major."[57] Since Ursa Major, the Great Bear, is close in the sky to the pole star, Edmund might be trying to show his own constancy. Critic Johnstone Parr reminds us that, in judicial astrology, "the constellations north of the zodiac have their respective influences, analogous to those of the planets…Ursa Major is like Mars, but the nebula under the tail resembles…Venus in its influence."[58] The warlike resemblance of Mars seems to fit Edmund's character, but one must be careful about Venus: the "nebula under the tail" of the bear most likely is the mass of faint stars of Coma Berenices, an entirely different constellation.

In *Romeo and Juliet*, there are so many astrological allusions that Shakespeare might have intended astral influence as a justification for this tragedy of apparent chance. Take the name of Mercutio, who has the temper of Mercury, and the Friar's apostrophe, in which he blames Capulet's misfortunes on the stars:

> *The heavens do lour upon you for some ill;*
> *Move them no more by crossing their high will.*[59]

It is possible that Shakespeare intended the stars to have a role in other tragedies of chance, especially *King Lear*, where astral influence plays a prominent role.

In *Troilus and Cressida*, Ulysses cries out:

> *The heavens themselves, the planets, and this centre,*
> *Observe degree, priority, and place,*
> *Insisture, course, proportion, season, form,*
> *Office, and custom, in all line of order;*
> *And therefore is this noble planet Sol*
> *In noble eminence enthron'd and spher'd*
> *Amidst the other, whose med'cinable eye*
> *Corrects the ill aspects of planets evil,*
> *And posts, like the commandment of a king,*
> *Sans check, to good and bad.*[60]

Shakespeare was superb at weaving into his plays the sum of contemporary beliefs about the heavens. *Troilus and Cressida* was written no later than 1609, the year before Galileo's observations of Jupiter but a time when the vast majority of Shakespeare's audience would have been happy with a cosmological system based on "the planets and this centre" Earth. The problem, according to one critic, is that astrology had a dual role as a hybrid science with its natural and judicial branches.[61] Shakespeare's avoidance of Copernican theory, coupled with his frequent allusions to judicial astrology, do not really mean that he had no interest in contemporary science. On the contrary, these allusions indicate a fascination with the eclipses and other scientific events of Shakespeare's day.

CHAPTER III

A
Changing Universe

adua, Italy, 1610: Imagine a large room with a high ceiling, a desk, and a chair. Seated in the chair is a middle-aged man named Galileo Galilei, one of the most prominent scientists of his time. He has just spent two nights observing the planet Jupiter with a small telescope; this is the first time a telescope has ever been used to look at the sky. Still not quite believing his own observations, he is completing his notes on the four moons he has discovered, four moons that revolve about Jupiter and not the Earth.

Galileo had put his telescope together only a year earlier, fashioning it from two spectacle lenses placed a certain distance apart. By looking through the two glass lenses, he could magnify distant objects. With his new telescope, Galileo made one astounding find after another—craters on the Moon, the phases of Venus, and spots on the Sun.

Galileo was right to question his own observation that day. Extraordinary claims, Carl Sagan would note centuries later, require extraordinary evidence; Galileo's discovery would be one of the most astonishing claims in the history of science. In just a few nights of observation, Galileo had seen the four moons circling Jupiter. The phases of Venus also could be explained only if that planet orbited the Sun, and not the Earth. If Galileo's observations were correct, there could be but one explanation: the Earth was not the center of the Universe.

LITERATURE RESPONDS TO THE NEW PHILOSOPHY

Although Galileo's observations brought the new ideas about Earth's position in the cosmos to the people, they were not the first indication of changing thought. Six decades earlier, Nicholas Copernicus, at the point of death, published *De Revolutionibus*. Appearing in 1543, this book set out a new way of looking at the heavens, with the Sun, not the Earth, at the center of the universe. *De Revolutionibus* was a sensation among the intellectuals of the time. It is interesting that the first political use of the word revolution appeared in the year 1600, to mean "a complete overthrow of the established government in any country or state by those who were previously subject to it."[62]

Galileo knew of Copernicus's work, and it was obvious to him that Ptolemy's system, which held that everything must revolve about the Earth, was no longer viable. He knew that Jupiter's family of moons proved that was right. However, he also knew that the time to defend Copernicus's vision had not come.

When *De Revolutionibus* was published, there was, in fact, plenty of observational evidence to support the idea that the Earth circled the Sun. The most

Nicholas Copernicus

obvious clue was that the stars rise and set some four minutes earlier each night, a small amount of time that quickly grows significant—half an hour's difference each week, and two hours each month.

The motion of the other planets through the sky is another line of evidence. Mars, Jupiter, and Saturn move in an eastward direction through the sky until they reach a certain place. Then they appear to slow down, almost stop, and next proceed westward for a period of a few months. Eventually this retrograde motion slows, then stops, and the planets resume their eastward pace. Though the reason for this would not have been apparent to people before the seventeenth century, it is evident now: in its orbit around the Sun, the Earth is overtaking the more distant, slower moving planets. The sensation is similar to that of a driver passing a slow car: as he overtakes the car, it seems to slow down and then move backwards relative to the passing driver.

The great meteor showers, their meteoroids crashing through the Earth's atmosphere like spokes in a wheel, also show that the Earth is pushing its way through space. However, this esoteric fact, along with the others just mentioned, would not have been apparent to observers before the seventeenth century. Even if Copernicus's contemporaries had understood these lines of reasoning, the general population would have found little meaning in them. Thus, as a theory, the Copernican idea attracted wide attention among scientists but not among the general public or those who followed the arts. Sir John Davies, a contemporary of Shakespeare, was an exception. He saw the new philosophy as a challenge to the magnificent cosmic dance he envisaged in his 1594 poem *Orchestra*. He gave the new ideas three lines in parentheses, and then concluded that the Ptolemaic Earth-centered system fit the order better:

> *Only the earth doth stand forever still:*
> *Her rocks remove not, nor her mountains meet;*
> *(Although some wits enrich'd with learning's skill*
> *Say heaven stands firm and that the Earth doth fleet*
> *And swiftly turneth underneath their feet)*
> *Yet, though the earth is ever steadfast seen,*
> *On her broad breast hath dancing ever been.*[63]

The important astronomical theme of *Orchestra* is that celestial bodies are dancing. In order to follow this dance we need to understand the details of the individual patterns, but how can we if the starting positions of the dance's most important partners, the Earth and the Sun, are uncertain? With the Moon orbiting about the Earth, both theories are in agreement, and Davies's poem captures their delicate orbit:

> *Who doth not see the measures of the Moon?*
> *Which thirteen times she danceth every year,*
> *And ends her pavan thirteen times as soon*
> *As doth her brother, of whose golden hair*
> *She borroweth part and proudly doth it wear.*
> *Then doth she coyly turn her face aside,*
> *That half her cheek is scarce sometimes descried.*[64]

Davies's poetic description of the Moon's phase needs no scientific change after four centuries. Her dance with her brother, the Sun, involves choreographed changing positions; she faces him at full phase, then turns her face aside as the phase wanes. Would that the rest of the dance could be so easily described!

Astronomical theories changed radically after Galileo's discoveries. Instead of a theoretical document, there was now a case of four moons that clearly did not revolve about the Earth. At the height of Galileo's career, this find was his greatest moment. It was also the beginning of his downfall.

THE NEW PHILOSOPHY AND FRANCIS BACON

During this same era, Francis Bacon was exploring a new way of looking at the natural world. He believed that ancient learning showed a shallow understanding of the world around us. This failure was not due to any lack of intellect in the minds of the ancient philosophers, but to the methods by which they built their ideas. Instead of relying on observations and experiments, these philosophers invoked instead the elegance of the argument itself. The philosopher with the most sensible reasoning, regardless of how well it related to observation, would win the day.

It is interesting to note that, for someone committed to the process of observation, Bacon enjoyed using the "old opinion" to buttress his own theoretical arguments when it was convenient for him. In his essay *Of Seditions and Troubles* Bacon writes: "When discords, and quarrels, and factions, are carried openly and audaciously, it is a sign the reverence of government is lost; for the motions of the greatest persons of a government ought to be as the motions of the planets under 'primum mobile' according to the old opinion, which is, that [each] of them is carried swiftly by the highest motion, and softly in their own motion; and therefore, when great ones in their own particular motion move violently…it is a sign the orbs are out of frame."[65] These words were written in 1625, long after Galileo made his observations.

Although Ptolemy's system was the tried and true order of the cosmos for 2000 years, it was showing its age, and Bacon knew it. To account for the motions of the planets too complex for basic Ptolemaic theory, the astronomers of the time invented epicycles, or circles within other circles. In his essay *Of Superstition*, written just two years after Galileo's discoveries, Bacon lamented that "The master of Superstition is the people, and in all Superstition wise men follow fools: …the schoolmen were like astronomers, which did feign eccentrics and epicycles, and such engines of orbs to save the phenomena, though they knew there were no such things…"[66] Bacon used the structure of Ptolemy when it fit his own arguments, but at his most passionate he demonstrated that its arguments were hollow.

Bacon's major writing, dated 1620, was *Novum Organum*, a remarkable work for its time; in fact, critic Jean-Marie Pousseur asked whether Bacon should be credited with being the father of all modern scientific reasoning because of this writing.[67] Bacon's work is very important because it focused on the need for all philosophers and scientists to do what some, like Tycho, Copernicus, and Galileo, had already been doing. Maybe it is more accurate, in these times, to say that Bacon was the agent, not the inventor, of the modern scientific method.

Francis Bacon

Bacon wrote of two ways of inductive reasoning: the sterile "anticipation of nature," conducted by the ancient and medieval philosophers, and the superior "interpretation of nature." Bacon held that it was not up to nature to conform to a philosopher's argument, but that it was up to the philosopher to understand nature through careful observation. Thanks to *Novum Organum*, science by experiment and observation, rather than by deductive reasoning and argument, had finally started along the path to respectability.

Science, however, still had quite a way to go before the rest of humanity accepted its new look. In 1611, the Catholic Church filed the first of several documents against Galileo—in secret and apparently without his knowledge. Five years later, the *Codex* against Galileo specified that any teaching that the Sun is in the center of heaven would be forbidden by the Church. Prudently, Galileo decided to wait until a more propitious time to defend the meaning of his sightings of Jupiter's moons. In 1623, Urban VIII, a modern thinker who seemed open to new ideas, was elected to the papacy. For a few years, Galileo walked and talked

Galileo

with the pontiff. Thinking that the time had come to speak out, late in 1629 he completed his *Dialogue Concerning the Two Chief World Systems*. One of the most important scientific works ever written, this book articulated Galileo's view of his telescope in the form of a debate. Imprudently, he created a character named Simplicio who parodied the Pope's ideas.

Urban VIII was infuriated. He felt that Galileo had taken advantage of his friendship, and that, through Simplicio, he was poking fun at the very core of Urban's papacy. The Pope put the old and virtually blind astronomer at the mercy of the Holy Office of the Inquisition. Threatened by the instruments of torture, Galileo was forced to "abandon the false opinion that the sun is the center of the world," and compelled to live out his days under house arrest. Galileo would never know how important a tool his telescope would become. Almost four centuries later, a giant version of his telescope would orbit the Earth, and a spacecraft named for him would visit the moons he discovered.

On November 10, 1979, Pope John Paul II asked that the 1633 conviction be annulled, saying that Galileo "had much to suffer, we cannot hide it, at the hands of men and the agencies of the church." However, since teaching the Copernican theory had been forbidden by the Congregation of the Index in 1616, it was possible that a new trial could find him guilty again. Thus it was suggested that the 1616 prohibition be reversed, and in 1992, it was reversed.

Galileo's discovery was a prime subject for consideration of the intellectuals of his time, and it was featured prominently in a poetic genre now known as philosophical poetry. Plato wrote of an "ancient quarrel between philosophy and poetry," and this quarrel flourished during the Renaissance. For most Renaissance writers, the poem by Lucretius, *De Rerum Natura (On the Nature of Things)*, written in the last century BC, is the model didactic poem, a work whose main purpose is to describe or explain the workings of the natural world and our perception of it.

The whole genre of philosophical poetry was based, to a varying extent, on Lucretius's work, and Galileo's discovery provided fresh material for this type of poetry. John Donne's *First Anniversary* appeared only one year after Galileo's

Jupiter observations, and it left no doubt that the new ideas had become prominent among serious philosophical poets who were concerned not only with changing views of the Universe, but also with mankind's role in that Universe:

> *And new philosophy calls all in doubt,*
> *The Element of fire is quite put out;*
> *The Sun is lost, and th' Earth, and no mans wit*
> *Can well direct him where to looke for it.*
> *And freely men confesse that this world's spent,*
> *When in the Planets, and the Firmament*
> *They seek so many new; they see that this*
> *Is crumbled out againe to his Atomies.*
> *Tis all in pieces, all cohaerence gone;*
> *All just supply, and all Relation:*
> *Prince, Subject, Father, Sonne, are things forgot,*
> *For every man alone thinks he hath got*
> *To be a Phoenix, and that then can bee*
> *None of that kinde, of which he is, but hee.*[68]

In 1653, John Donne wrote satirically about Copernicus in *Ignatius His Conclave*, in which Ignatius enters Hell, sees all the rooms, and finds a man. "As soon as the door creaked," he notes, "I spied a certain mathematician, which till then had been busied to find, to deride, to detrude Ptolemy, and now with an erect countenance and settled pace came to the gates,…beat the doors, and cried, 'Are these shut against me, to whom all the Heavens were ever open; who was a soul to the Earth, and gave it motion?'"

After some thought, Lucifer answers, "what cares…whether the earth travel or stand still? Hath your raising up of the earth into heaven brought men to that confidence that they build new towers or threaten God again? Or do they, out of this motion of the earth, conclude that there is no Hell, or deny the punishment of sin? Do not men believe? Do they not live just as they did before? Besides, this detracts from the dignity of your learning, and derogates from your right and title of coming to this place, that those opinions of yours may very well be true…Let therefore this little mathematician, dread Emperor, withdraw himself to his own company…"

Lucifer signified his assent, and Copernicus, without muttering a word, was as quiet as he thinks the sun.[69]

Donne was not alone in his worry that all coherence was gone, that the natural order was giving way to disorder. The Renaissance poet that went furthest in trying to explain the clockwork cycles of the heavens, as Copernicus saw them, was Henry More, who penned in 1647:

> *And as the Planets in our world (of which*
> *the Suns the heart and kernel) do receive*
> *Their nightly light from Suns that do enrich*
> *Their sable mantle with bright gemmes, and give*
> *A goodly splendour, and sad men relieve*
> *With their fair twinkling rayes, so our worlds Sunne*
> *Becomes a starre elsewhere, and doth derive*
> *Joynt light with others, cheareth all that won*
> *In those dim duskith Orbs round other Suns that run.*[70]

Although Galileo sensed that history would be on his side, John Milton was not so sure. The poet was planning an epic about the creation of the world and the fall of man, and he conversed with Galileo about the nature of the solar system. In 1674, long after Galileo's death, Milton published *Paradise Lost*; in Book VIII Adam asks about the Nature of the Earth, and he seems to suspect that the Earth is not the center of the Universe:

> *When I behold this goodly Frame, this World*
> *Of Heav'n and Earth consisting, and compute*
> *Thir magnitudes, this Earth a spot, a grain,*
> *An Atom, with the Firmament compar'd*
> *And all her number'd Stars, that seem to roll*
> *Spaces incomprehensible (for such*
> *Thir distance argues and thir swift return*
> *Diurnal) merely to officiate light*
> *Round this opacous Earth, this punctual spot,*

One day and night; in all thir vast survey
Useless besides; reasoning I oft admire,
How Nature wise and frugal could commit
Such disproportions, with superfluous hand
So many nobler Bodies to create,
Greater so manifold to this one use,
For aught appears, and on thir Orbs impose
Such restless revolution day by day
Repeated, while the sedentary Earth,
That better might with far less compass move,
Serv'd by more noble than herself, attains
Her end without least motion, and receives,
As Tribute such a sumless journey brought
Of incorporeal speed, her warmth and light;
Speed, to describe whose swiftness Number fails.

What is important about this reference to Earth's role in the universe is not which side Milton is on—*Paradise Lost* does not make that clear—but that the issue is important enough that Milton has Adam discuss it with the angel Raphael.

SEVENTEENTH AND EIGHTEENTH CENTURIES

To think that science and poetry are two disciplines that are properly divorced from each other is to lose sight of what each is about and what their common goal is. In their highest forms, both are avenues of inquiry into the human condition and its relationship to the Universe. Knowing what that Universe is and how it is structured is fundamental to each.

By the mid-seventeenth century, telescopes were providing tremendous new insights into the solar system. In 1656, Christiaan Huygens (who a year later would invent the first pendulum clock) discovered that Saturn is circled by a ring. He announced his find in an anagram, his sentence gutted into a series of letters. When reconstructed, his discovery sentence reads:

Annulo cingitur, tennui, plano, nusquam coherente, ad eclipticam inclinato.

Loosely translated, this means:

It is surrounded by a thin, flat, ring, nowhere touching, inclined to the ecliptic.

Not only was Earth accompanied by a series of other worlds orbiting the Sun, but also these worlds were becoming more interesting and esoteric. By 1700, telescopes were common enough that astronomers around the world were becoming familiar with them.

Could it have been an accident of history that two of the greatest scientific minds in history spun their magic at the same time and at the same place? For it was Edmond Halley and Isaac Newton who chatted one day about planets, comets, and gravity. Halley had examined records of comets going back two centuries or more. From some 85 comets that appeared between 1500 and 1700, Halley had the genius to pick out the fact that three comet apparitions were separated by about 76 years. The comets in question appeared in 1531, 1607, and one Halley witnessed himself, in 1682. He told Newton about this discovery, and went on to propose that the three were return visits of the same comet.

This news from Halley could not have reached Newton at a better moment, and he replied that he was working on a little project that might shed light on Halley's question. Newton's work turned out to be his *Principia Mathematica*, in which he established his laws about how worlds move about the Sun.

With its once-in-a-lifetime schedule, Halley's Comet brings generations together. The potential for grandparent and grandchild to stand together to look at Halley's Comet is repeated every 76 years at the comet loops around the Sun, returning, in a sense, to check on the progress of civilization. Its visit highlighted the defeat of Attila the Hun in 451 and terrified the warriors of the Norman conquest of England in 1066. We can see Halley's comet pictured on the tapestry in a church in Bayeux, France, that commemorated the conquest. It returned in 1456 and 1531, and in 1607 some bold families saw it as they were starting new lives in the new world. It was on its following trip around in 1682 that the comet was observed by Edmond Halley himself. Halley did not live to see the triumph of his prediction. The comet's appearance on Christmas night of 1758 was the final proof that it was a wandering cousin of the Earth, orbiting as a prisoner of the gravity of the Sun.

The eighteenth century brought continuing advances to our knowledge of the sky, thanks largely to constant improvements being made in telescopes. By 1781, William Herschel was well into a survey of the heavens. On March 17 of that year, Herschel noticed a strange object in the constellation of Gemini, an object that turned out to be the first planet discovered in historic times. After the discovery of Herschel's planet, later named Uranus, telescopes became increasingly popular in England, which led to innovations in the instruments. George Adams and his son made a series of beautiful reflectors, with metal mirrors mounted in brass tubes. Jesse Ramsden and John Dolland crafted small refractors, with lenses that focused the light at an eyepiece at the opposite end of the tube in the style of Galileo's telescope. Standing in line to look through one of these telescopes became a popular evening activity, and, depending on the quality of the telescope and the skill of the person using it, the views ranged from disappointing to superb. In 1806 William Wordsworth commented on the crowd trying to look through a telescope in his poem *Star Gazers*:

Not till the fire is dying in the grate,
Look we for any kinship with the stars.

George Meredith, *Modern Love*, iv [T]

On July 18, 1994, fragment G collided with Jupiter at a speed of 60 kilometers per second. NASA's Hubble Space Telescope recorded this magnificent view of the resulting plume of material that rose some 3000 kilometers into Jupiter's atmosphere after the collision.

> *Whatever be the cause, tis sure that they who pry and pore*
> *Seem to meet with little gain, seem less happy than before:*
> *One after one they take their turn, nor have I one espied*
> *That doth not slackly go away, as if dissatisfied.*[71]

It has been my most serious goal, when showing first-time viewers through a telescope, that they do not leave dissatisfied. The solution now, as in 1806, is in the choice of celestial object to view. A star or galaxy would not have been too impressive as seen through the small eyepieces of Wordsworth's time. However, the Moon should have looked magnificent, then as now. For young children, I sometimes stand at the telescope so that I can see the beam of moonlight actually enter the child's eye. In this manner I make sure that the first look is so successful that even Wordsworth would have been satisfied.

As the nineteenth century went on, mankind's understanding of the heavens, especially the solar system, continued to leap forward. We began to see the Earth as one planet among seven very different worlds. In 1846, John Couch Adams of England and Urbain Leverrier of France independently completed the mathematics that led to the discovery of an eighth world called Neptune. At the same time, Charles Darwin was studying life forms on the Galapagos Islands off the coast of Ecuador, and developing his seminal work, *The Origin of Species*. Once again our ideas of a neighborhood of worlds, and of the development of life on one of these worlds, were undergoing significant change. As we shall see in the next chapter, England's great poet, Alfred Lord Tennyson, captured this golden moment in civilization when he wrote these lines in 1850:

> *Ring out, wild bells, to the wild sky,*
> *The flying cloud, the frosty light:*
> *The year is dying in the night;*
> *Ring out, wild bells, and let him die.*

> *Ring out the old, ring in the new,*
> *Ring, happy bells, across the snow:*
> *The year is going, let him go;*
> *Ring out the false, ring in the true.*[72]

CHAPTER IV

Ring Out, Wild Bells

It would have been hard to predict that Alfred Tennyson, the son of a rector in a town on England's east coast, would become one of science's greatest expositors—a man who captured the essence of the greatest scientific achievements of the nineteenth century, and then returned them to the world through the words and rhymes of his poetry. During his years at Trinity College, Cambridge, Tennyson joined an intellectual group called the Apostles, and he thoroughly enjoyed the conversations he had with his friends there. But when his closest friend in that group, Arthur Henry Hallam, died unexpectedly in 1833, the young poet, stunned, became depressed and stopped publishing for almost a decade. He did not give up, however: when his writing returned, it was stronger and more mature. In 1837 he read Lyell's famous *Principles of Geology*, in which the broad outlines of the evolution of the Earth were first proposed—principles that would soon find a home in Tennyson's poems. By the 1840s, Tennyson let his lively interest in the night sky permeate his writing, as we see in his 1847 *The Princess*:

> *Now lies the Earth all Danae to the stars,*
> *And all thy heart lies open unto me.*
> > *Now slides the silent meteor on, and leaves*
> > *A shining furrow, as thy thoughts in me.*[73]

During these years Tennyson was slowly building his masterpiece. In 1850, at the height of Tennyson's career, *In Memoriam* appeared. This was the same year he was married and was named poet laureate. *In Memoriam* was far more than an elegy to Hallam. One of the truly great poems of English literature, *In Memoriam* begins as a memorial but ends as a celebration of mid-19th century life, and of the unprecedented scientific advances of that time. As one critic suggested, the poem's most profound achievement was to domesticate science, to bring it to the level of a wide readership, and to attach to it a moral and religious interpretation. It represents the highwater mark for Tennyson's enthusiasm for introducing scientific concepts into poetry, both in the amount of scientific information presented and in its poetic effectiveness.[74] Tennyson used the facts of science to enrich the language of poetry, as in the following example:[75]

Alfred, Lord Tennyson

> *Who loves not Knowledge? Who shall rail*
> *Against her beauty? May she mix*
> *With men and prosper! Who shall fix*
> *Her pillars? Let her work prevail.*[76]

Who indeed should set the pillars of Hercules, the limits of knowledge? Six cantos later, Tennyson suggests an answer:

> *Let Science prove we are, and then,*
> *What matters Science unto men,*
> *At least to me. I would not stay.*[77]

To understand the powerful role of science, particularly astronomy and evolution, in this poem, it helps to know that *In Memoriam* grew out of a collection of elegies written as the expression of agony at the loss of a friend. It was not assembled into the masterwork we know until Tennyson realized he had written so many elegies. "It is the story of a soul stunned by a tremendous loss," notes one critic, "and struggling to find the meaning of a universe in which such losses can occur."[78]

How common a sentiment this is! We all have suffered tragic losses, and when we do we tend to question the natural order that allows such things to happen. (Would that the rest of us had Tennyson's skill to deal with loss in such a profound way.) *In Memoriam* goes further: it reflects the strength of its author's love of careful research into the sciences and theology. "He lacked and distrusted the passion of the revolutionary," this critic notes, "for creating and imposing exclusive ideas of truth by skipping inconvenient evidence." Tennyson insisted on submitting the ideas of the emerging scientific thought "to the test of his own feelings and his own vision."[79]

At the start of *In Memoriam*, Tennyson puts into words his grief at the loss of his friend, but at the same time he wishes to write about a Universe that brings such grief. The words from his pen are an imperfect tool for this purpose, but Nature also seems to him to be structured the same way, partly to give answers, and partly to raise questions.

> *I sometimes hold it half a sin*
> > *To put in words the grief I feel;*
> > *For words, like Nature, half reveal*
> *And half conceal the Soul within.*[80]

Wordcraft is the poet's basic tool, and Tennyson's pen is strong enough to suggest a vision of the Universe. Tennyson's vision will see the Earth both as the familiar world we live in, and as a small body in space.

> *This round of green, this orb of flame,*
> > *Fantastic beauty; such as lurks*
> > *In some wild poet, when he works*
> *Without a conscience or an aim.*[81]

As the poem twists and turns, its words occasionally paint a picture of a natural scene that takes this "fantastic beauty" and puts it to work:

> *We talk'd: the stream beneath us ran,*
> *The wine flask lying couch'd in moss,*

Or cool'd within the glooming wave;
And last, returning from afar,
Before the crimson-circled star
Had fallen into her father's grave,

And brushing ankle-deep in flowers,
We heard behind the woodbine veil
The milk that bubbled in the pail,
And buzzings of the honeyed hours.[82]

The Sun has set at the end of the day, and with the end of twilight a bright planet (the crimson-circled star) is following her father, the Sun, in setting

In Memoriam is far more than a description of Nature as elegant natural beauty. The poem is also a serious attempt to look at the scientific world of Tennyson's time, and it deals with scientific issues in remarkable detail. In the following passage, Sorrow, the priestess, suggests a pattern for the Universe:

O Sorrow, cruel fellowship,
O Priestess in the vaults of Death,
O sweet and bitter in a breath,
What whispers from thy lying lip?

"The stars," she whispers, "blindly run;
A web is woven across the sky;
From out waste places comes a cry,
And murmurs from the dying sun;

And all the phantom, Nature, stands—
With all the music in her tone,
A hollow echo of my own—
A hollow form with empty hands."

And shall I take a thing so blind,
Embrace her as my natural good;

> *Or crush her, like a vice of blood,*
> *Upon the threshhold of the mind?*[83]

Tennyson mistrusts a Universe which seems to follow a random course with no order or pattern. It is the same mistrust that John Davies noted in *Orchestra* (see chapter 3), by placing the new cosmology in parentheses (see chapter one) so that it would not interfere with the cosmic dance of *Orchestra*. The new cosmology seems a random, cold, and silent universe in which Man's prayers are unheard:

> *Man, her last work, who seemed so fair,*
> > *Such splendid purpose in his eyes,*
> > *Who roll'd the psalm to wintry skies,*
> *Who built him fanes of fruitless prayer,*
>
> *Who trusted God was love indeed*
> > *And love Creation's final law—*
> > *Tho' Nature, red in tooth and claw*
> *With ravine, shriek'd against his creed—*
>
> *Who lov'd, who suffer'd countless ills*
> > *Who battled for the True, the Just,*
> > *Be blown about the desert dust,*
> *Or seal'd within the iron hills?*[84]

Sixteen years after the publication of *In Memoriam*, Gerard Manley Hopkins, a poet whose work we will explore in the next chapter, probed the mysteries of the night sky and asked:

> *God, though to Thee our psalm we raise*
> *No answering voice comes from the skies;*
> *To Thee the trembling sinner prays*
> *But no forgiving voice replies;*
> *Our prayer seems lost in desert ways,*
> *Our hymn in the vast silence dies.*[85]

Both poets wrote from a strong sense of God, coupled with a profound wonder at the sky. The cry from a dying Sun invoked by Tennyson in the stanza beginning, "The stars...blindly run" harks back to the nebular hypothesis, the favored theory, in that time, of how the solar system began. Formulated by Pierre Simon, Marquis de Laplace, this hypothesis held that the planets are children of the Sun, formed of the outskirts of the cloud whose center became the Sun. If that theory is correct, then the Sun is slowly losing its heat and will someday die. Although that will happen, the Sun will retain its current basic state for five billion years. What I find more interesting than this idea is the one expressed in the first statement from *Sorrow* that the stars blindly run to weave a web across the sky. In one interpretation of "blindly," Tennyson suggests that objects in the sky do not obey an intelligence but the celestial mechanics worked out by Newton, whose laws of gravitation described how objects travel through space.[86] Yet to me, this interpretation does not seem plausible. *Sorrow* describes a celestial system where nothing works right, and thus the blind running of the stars is meant to suggest cosmic anarchy.

References to the nebular hypothesis appear throughout *In Memoriam*, even at places where it is invoked peripherally, as with the eddies of gas involved in the formation of the planets, appearing again in Canto 128:

> *No doubt vast eddies in the flood*
> *Of onward time shall yet be made:*[87]

Laplace published his outline of the nebular hypothesis a generation before Tennyson wrote these lines of *In Memoriam*. Struck by the similarity of motion and direction of our solar system, he proposed, in 1796, a theory that the Sun and planets condensed out of a cloud. As it rotated, it would throw off a series of concentric rings, each of which condensed into a planet. Although it resembles an idea that Immanuel Kant set forth in 1755, the Laplace theory probably was developed independently and with far greater detail. It was possible, some thought, that the nebulae that were being discovered across the sky were faroff examples of solar systems in formation. By the 1830s, the whole question of the nature of the nebulae was in its infancy: we knew of the objects described by Charles Messier, the famous comet discoverer who cataloged more than 100 comets as part of his search of the night sky, and many others listed by William Herschel. It was only in the twentieth century that we have unveiled them for what they really are: clusters of stars, clouds of gas and dust, and the distant galaxies of our expanding universe.

With his theory, Laplace was surprisingly close to providing the understanding of the solar system's genesis which persists today. The solar system, astronomers now think, began as a large dark cloud in space, sitting passively for an incredibly long time. Known as a giant molecular cloud, it was more than 300 light years across—one of the biggest objects in the galaxy. Somewhere nearby a massive star exploded, lighting the sky as a supernova and spreading carbon into nearby space and into the giant molecular cloud. With the injection of carbon, and with the possible help of some ultraviolet irradiation, the cloud slowly began to evolve into a different place, becoming more organized and starting to rotate. Its center grew hot and massive, and became the Sun. In surrounding parts of the cloud, clumps of material accreted to one another to form the planets.

Laplace's theory suggested an ordered Universe, but Tennyson's *Sorrow* still saw stars blindly running. In the years before the completion of *In Memoriam*, several bright comets had "blindly run" their courses, in a sense, to weave a web across the sky. The Great Comet of 1811, which will be discussed in chapter 7, was one such comet. Eight years later, a second bright comet rounded the Sun. However, the appearance of a great comet in 1830, just three years before Tennyson first penned this group of stanzas, and another in 1831—two great comets in as many years—was highly unusual and might have added credence to Tennyson's image of objects blindly crossing the sky. Although the first of these two comets attracted some attention, when it was brightest the 1830 comet was visible only from the southern hemisphere, heading north. The second comet appeared a few months later, and was first seen over England with a bright, short tail.

Halley's comet passed over the sky of Earth in 1835, and a magnificent comet appeared in 1843. It dominated the evening sky throughout the world that March, and as it completed its hairpin encounter with the Sun, it grew a tail that stretched for 70 million miles, almost as long as the distance between the Sun and Earth.

In 1846, a fainter comet appeared, a periodic comet whose course astronomers thought they understood well. However, as it moved through the sky it split into two pieces. At the time, a comet splitting into two was an unknown event, difficult to explain, one which could have inspired a thought about objects blindly running about the sky. (Comets are now seen to split apart with some frequency, and these events are dramatic. By far the most spectacular example of a comet's breaking up occurred in July, 1992, when, unseen by anyone on Earth, Comet Shoemaker-Levy 9 broke apart as a result of an intense encounter with Jupiter. When the comet was discovered in March, 1993, its 21 pieces were described as a string of pearls. The comet fragments collided with Jupiter in July, 1994. See chapter 7.)

Other major events were also taking place in astronomy at the time. In 1846, two astronomers, John Couch Adams from England, and Urbain Leverrier from France, independently calculated where the eighth planet should lie. Finally, Johann Galle and Heinrich d'Arrest in Germany turned their telescope to the proper location and discovered the planet. Four years later, Tennyson alluded to the event, with "arms" referring to telescopes:

> *A time to sicken and to swoon,*
> *When Science reaches forth her arms*
> *To feel from world to world, and charms*
> *Her secret from the latest moon?*[88]

Besides Neptune, which was hardly a moon, some notable new moons were discovered during the middle years of the nineteenth century. William Lassell discovered Triton, orbiting Neptune, in 1846, the year of Neptune's discovery. Hyperion, the seventh of Saturn's moons, was detected by Harvard's George Bond in 1848, two years before the publication of *In Memoriam*. Ariel and Umbriel were found orbiting Uranus in 1851, by William Lassell. Also, between 1801 and 1849 the first ten asteroids were detected.[89] This was the new science, a litany of observations and ideas that were changing the way we look at ourselves, like the sunspots which wander like isles of night across the blinding Sun:

> *And was the day of my delight*
> *As pure and perfect as I say?*
> *The very source and fount of day*
> *Is dash'd with wandering isles of night.*[90]

The process of scientific discovery is a slow and delicate one. Although Galileo first detected sunspots in 1610, observers watched the Sun for another 200 years before Heinrich Schwabe, an amateur astronomer from Dessau, Germany, bought a small refractor telescope in 1826. With it he began to observe the Sun in hopes of finding the elusive planet Vulcan crossing in front of the solar surface. The planet did not exist, but in 1843, Schwabe announced the existence of a cycle of sunspot activity lasting about a decade. In the story of the discovery of Neptune, the calculations of both Adams and Leverrier were not taken seriously at first. George Airy, England's astronomer royal, simply did not believe Adams, and LeVerrier had to find astronomers on his own—Johanne Galle and Heinrich d'Arrest—who were willing to conduct the search that led to the discovery. It is the beautiful process of discovery and learning that Tennyson refers to in Canto 23:

> *When each by turns was guide to each,*
> > *And Fancy light from Fancy caught,*
> > *And Thought leapt out to wed with Thought*
> *Ere Thought could wed itself with Speech;*[91]

We also know that wherever we are, our scientific understanding is just at a beginning. Even more of a beginning is how we, on this small world, relate to the grand scheme. In one of *In Memoriam*'s most exquisite passages, Tennyson looks upon humankind as babes wandering about in the woods, insisting that we do not yet know how to think of ourselves in the Universe:

> *O, yet we trust that somehow good*
> > *Will be the final goal of ill,*
> > *To pangs of nature, sins of will,*
> *Defects of doubt, and taints of blood;*

> *That nothing walks with aimless feet;*
> > *That not one life shall be destroy'd,*
> > *Or cast as rubbish to the void,*
> *When God hath made the pile complete;*

> *That not a worm is cloven in vain,*
> > *That not a moth with vain desire*

> *Is shrivell'd in a fruitless fire,*
> *Or but subserves another's gain.*
>
> *Behold, we know not anything;*
> > *I can but trust that good shall fall*
> > *At last—far off—at last, to all,*
> *And every winter change to spring.*
>
> *So runs my dream, but what am I?*
> > *An infant crying in the night;*
> > *An infant crying for the light,*
> *And with no language but a cry.*[92]

This powerful thought reflects the emotions of some of us who have spent years gazing at the sky, or studying some other aspect of nature. On a dark night the sky does seem peaceful, even benevolent. It is hard to avoid connecting a starry night with the thought that all is right with the universe, and that good shall ultimately fall, and that every winter shall indeed turn to spring. But then comes our "reality check:" Nature is neutral, and we cannot begin to understand the meaning, if there is one, of a dark and lovely night. We are literally still infants crying in this night, in a Universe so complex and vast that we can't even put the question into proper words. In that sense, Tennyson's prescient lines seek at least to frame the state of our ability to ask the question.

Canto 118 gives poetic voice to the biological breakthrough that was taking place at the very same period that Tennyson was composing *In Memoriam*. Charles Darwin's studies on the Galapagos Islands led to *The Origin of Species*, his great contribution to our understanding of our heritage and ancestry. Darwin's work led to the idea that life forms evolve from earlier forms, and that the Earth itself has evolved though time:

> *Contemplate all this work of Time,*
> > *The giant laboring in his youth;*
> > *Nor dream of human love and truth,*
> *As dying Nature's earth and lime;*

But trust that those we call the dead
  Are breathers of an ampler day
  For ever nobler ends. They say,
The solid earth whereon we tread

In tracts of fluent heat began,
  And grew to seeming-random forms,
  The seeming prey of cyclic storms,
Till at the last arose the man;

Who throve and branch'd from clime to clime,
  The herald of a higher race,
  And of himself in higher place,
If so he type this work of time

Within himself, from one to more;
  Or, crown'd with attributes of woe
  Like glories, move his course, and show
That life is not as idle ore,

But iron dug from central gloom,
  And heated hot with burning fears,
  And dipt in baths of hissing tears,
And batter'd with the shocks of doom

To shape and use. Arise and fly
  The reeling Faun, the sensual feast;
  Move upward, working out the beast,
And let the ape and tiger die.[93]

Tennyson's enthusiasm for evolution is tempered by his belief that some teleological force has control over the process, letting the lower life forms fall away. Noting that the ape and tiger die, Tennyson crowns evolution with a sense of divine purpose; the evolution of the Earth is reproduced by the development of life. This is a theme that recurs in his other poetry, for example in *Maud*, which appeared five years after *In Memoriam:*

> *So many a million of ages have gone to the making of man:*
> *He now is first, but is he the last? is he not too base?*
>
> *The man of science himself is fonder of glory, and vain,*
> *An eye well-practised in nature, a spirit bounded and poor;*
> *The passionate heart of the poet is whirl'd into folly and vice.*
> *I would not marvel at either, but keep a temperate brain;*
> *For not to desire or admire, if a man could learn it, were more*
> *Than to walk all day like the sultan of old in a garden of spice.*[94]

In staking out the grounds of his theory of evolution, Charles Darwin proposed two ideas. One was evolution itself, which says that humans moved upward, working out the beast. The second was natural selection, Darwin's proposed mechanism to explain how evolution takes place. While scientists generally agree on the first, there is hot debate about the second. According to Darwin's basic theory of natural selection, species evolve gradually, without sudden change. However, evidence now exists for a series of bursts of new species. As we shall see in chapter 7, a comet or asteroid impact, or a series of damaging volcanic eruptions, could trigger such a burst.

The best known such impact took place 65 million years ago. In just a few minutes, an Earth teeming with many forms of life was turned into a burning wasteland. The change that occurred at the end of the Cretaceous period of Earth's history was anything but gradual. With large thunderclaps and a huge crash, a comet (or possibly an asteroid) slammed into the Earth on what is now Mexico's Yucatan Peninsula. Kilometers-high walls of water raced out from the point of impact, and millions of tons of dust surged upwards in a gigantic cloud. A crater at least 150 kilometers wide and several kilometers deep was formed in less than a minute, and excavated material from the crater rushed out with such force that it quickly circled the Earth. As the Earth's surface was blitzed with debris, temperatures rose as high as those in a broiling oven, setting off a worldwide firestorm. Within a few weeks, the whole planet was shrouded in a cloud of dust and soot. The sky was absolutely black, and for over a month there was no sunlight whatsoever, anywhere on Earth. The rain was dense with sulfuric acid.

Finally, as the clouds dissipated, Earth was left with a global warming period that lasted for centuries.

By the time the episode was over, more than three quarters of the species of life on Earth had vanished. Although Tennyson was not aware of Earth's great cataclysm, he did know that at one time dinosaurs roamed the Earth, and that they were now extinct:

> *There rolls the deep where grew the tree.*
> *O earth, what changes hast thou seen!*
> *There where the long street roars hath been*
> *The stillness of the central sea.*
>
> *The hills are shadows, and they flow*
> *From form to form, and nothing stands;*
> *They melt like mist, the solid lands,*
> *Like clouds they shape themselves and go.*[95]

The only thing unchanging about the Earth is that it is always changing. Where once there were seas, mountains appear, and the mountains of long ago eroded down to hills and valleys. Our understanding of this continuity is not new; even the author of *Ecclesiastes* wrote of the majesty of Earth's water cycle, and of other cycles of change in Earth's history:

> *All the rivers run into the sea; yet the sea is not full; unto the place from whence the rivers come, thither they return again.*
>
> *The thing that hath been, it is that which shall be; and that which is done is that which shall be done: and there is no new thing under the sun.*[96]

In Canto 121, Tennyson seems to be having some fun with the poetic invocation of Hesper and Phosphor, the ancient Greek names for Venus as the evening star and the morning star. Bringing epic tradition up to date means asserting that the two stars are really a single planet, Venus. As Hesper, Venus never sets long after the Sun. Tennyson knows that Phosphor can never rise during the same night; Venus is either one or the other for periods of several months at a time. But when Phosphor does rise, the "greater light" of the Sun cannot be far behind.

> *Sad Hesper o'er the buried sun*
> > *And ready, thou, to die with him,*
> > *Thou watchest all things ever dim*
> *And dimmer, and a glory done.*
> ...
>
> *Bright Phosphor, fresher for the night,*
> > *By thee the world's great work is heard*
> > *Beginning, and the wakeful bird;*
> *Behind thee comes the greater light.*

Finally, Tennyson reveals, in the climax of this canto, that the dual evening and morning star are really one:

> *Sweet Hesper-Phosphor, double name*
> > *For what is one, the first, the last,*
> > *Thou, like my present and my past,*
> *Thy place is changed; thou art the same.*[97]

Alfred, Lord Tennyson was a poet whose works were strengthened by repeated references to the natural world. The beauty of the night sky, as his 1842 poem *Locksley Hall* so effectively shows, was a central part of that marriage between poetry and the night sky.

> *Many a night from yonder ivied casement, ere I went to rest,*
> *Did I look on great Orion sloping slowly to the west.*
> *Many a night I saw the Pleiads, rising thro' the mellow shade,*
> *Glitter like a swarm of fire-flies tangled in a silver braid.*[98]

As much as it was one of Tennyson's greatest poetic achievements, *In Memoriam* was a scientific achievement as well, for it presented the accomplishments of the science of the time to a wide readership of culturally sophisticated people who were not scientists. But to claim that *In Memoriam* was a poetic explanation of science is to limit its awesome power. The opus did not seek to explain the scientific accomplishments of the day so much as to humanize and romanticize the scientific accomplishments. Although many poets wrote of the night sky, it was Tennyson who tried to connect the romance of the sky with the accompanying scientific theories, and in doing so, he created a poetic legacy that helped to change the focus of later writing.

Is the sky a means by which we humans can see the extent of our dreams, the limit of what is possible, and even the boundless limit of the horizon of our soul? Is this the major discovery of those who share a passion for the night sky? Perhaps. We give the last word to Matthew Arnold, who suggests that the function of poetry is to ring out this thought:

> *Plainness and clearness without shadow of stain!*
> *Clearness divine!*
> *Ye heavens, whose pure dark regions have no sign*
> *Of languor, though so calm, and, though so great,*
> *Are yet untroubled and yet unpassionate;*
> *Who, though so noble, share in the world's toil,*
> *And, though so task'd, keep free from dust and soil!*
> *I will not say that your mild deeps retain*
> *A tinge, it may be, of their silent pain*
> *Who have long'd deeply once, and long'd in vain—*
> *But I will rather say that you remain*
> *A world above man's head, to let him see*
> *How boundless might his soul's horizons be,*
> *How vast, yet of what clear transparency!*
> *How it were good to abide there, and breathe free;*
> *How fair a lot to fill*
> *Is left to each man still!*[99]

CHAPTER V

A Poem and a Comet [100]

August 4, 1864: a clear, dark sky. Although both Jupiter and Saturn had set, Mars was in the constellation of Aries, high in the south, its dark features visible through a telescope.[101] Auriga and Taurus were both high in the east. The Moon, having just passed its new phase, did not disturb the darkness. While vacationing in Wales that summer, a young Oxford student named Gerard Manley Hopkins might have observed this scene in those pre-dawn hours. For all the beauty of that sky, though, Hopkins's gaze was drawn toward the second magnitude star Beta Tauri. Just west of that star shone the bright head of Tempel's comet, and its tail stretched toward another star almost as bright as the first, the nearby Iota Aurigae. The comet was moving relatively quickly, completing its quick dash past Sun and Earth within two weeks.

On September 13, 1864, less than a month after the speeding comet had faded from naked-eye view, Hopkins wrote these lines:

> *— I am like a slip of comet,*
> *Scarce worth discovery, in some corner seen*
> *Bridging the slender difference of two stars,*
> *Come out of space, or suddenly engender'd*
> *By heady elements, for no man knows:*
> *But when she sights the sun she grows and sizes*
> *And spins her skirts out, while her central star*

Shakes its cocooning mists; and so she comes
To fields of light; millions of travelling rays
Pierce her; she hangs upon the flame-cased sun
And sucks the light as full as Gideon's fleece:
But then her tether calls her; she falls off,
And as she dwindles shreds her smock of gold
Amidst the sistering planets, till she comes
To single Saturn, last and solitary;
And then goes out into the cavernous dark.
So I go out: my little sweet is done:
I have drawn heat from this contagious sun:
To not ungentle death now forth I run.[102]

Did Hopkins really see that predawn sky? We do not know. But even at that young age, he was a thorough scholar and a careful observer, and his poems reflect his keen powers of observation. Set in the Renaissance, when "single Saturn" was indeed the outermost known planet, the poem above was intended to be a speech from a play entitled *Floris in Italy*.

The speaker, Giulia, is one of a number of people attracted to Floris, and Hopkins intended the image of the comet as Giulia's farewell soliloquy to Floris. Just as the Sun doesn't care about the planets and comets that orbit it, Floris does not recognize Giulia's worth, looking instead toward her cousin. Hopkins changed an early draft—"But when it sights the sun" to "But when she sights the sun" to strengthen the feminine metaphors of the comet image.[103] Like a stylish square dancer circling right or left around the square, Giulia "spins her skirts out" in a brave but unsuccessful attempt to win Floris, and as Giulia feels her distance from Floris growing, she falls off, shedding her smock of gold.

Hopkins was committed to the idea that every object in nature has its own individualizing quality. He called this special quality inscape; a comet, for example, has a pattern that is unique to it. This pattern is not just the comet's form but its inner substance and its behavior as well. The more carefully we observe a comet, the more we perceive its inscape. The response that perception invokes in us is called *instress*. Although his comet poem appeared before Hopkins developed these intriguing ideas, its lines clearly show that Hopkins saw a special relationship between the comet's appearance and its behavior. Thus it makes sense to try to understand the comet of Hopkins's poem in relation to real comets that he might have observed, and to the rich tradition that they represent.

As we noticed in chapter 4, the 1840s were a fertile time for comets, and the night skies in the years preceding Hopkins's poem were even more lavish. In 1858, Donati's comet swung around the Sun with a long tail curving across a large segment of the evening sky; the famous American astronomer, George Bond, stood on the terrace of Harvard's new observatory and gazed at this ghostly marvel in the night. Only three years later, John Tebbutt, an amateur astronomer from New South Wales, sighted a comet that was moving rapidly northward. By July of 1861, this comet had a nucleus as bright as a first magnitude star, and had grown a protracted tail stretching over two-thirds of the visible sky. The comet caused a sensation in London's newspapers, which provided detailed reports and drawings of it. A year later, Comet Swift-Tuttle appeared with a rare spike directed toward the Sun, and a series of jets seemed to erupt from the comet's center. (This comet later became famous as the parent of the annual Perseid meteor stream; appearing each August, the stream consists of dust particles from this comet.) A full contemporary account of this comet appeared, curiously enough, in *Cornhill*, a literary magazine widely read by the intellectuals of the mid-nineteenth century.[104] Having enjoyed the magazine since his youth, Hopkins was one of its avid readers.

PORTRAIT BY RITA MACKENZIE

Gerard Manley Hopkins

On July 4, 1864, Ernst Tempel, from Marseilles, France, discovered a comet moving northeast through the constellation of Aries; an observer named Respighi independently found the comet on the next night from Bologna, Italy. Within a month it became fairly bright; on August 8, it passed only about 15 million kilometers from Earth, about the same distance as Comet Hyakutake in 1996. I suspect that Hopkins concentrated on Comet Tempel, which was fresh in his memory, but that he mingled recollections of all these comets when he wrote *I am like a slip of comet....* Hopkins implies that at this early stage, the comet is fragile and small, "scarce worth discovery." How true these words ring! All my own comets were faint when I first saw them, appearing as faint fuzzy patches of light, some barely brighter than the background of sky behind them.

The more I studied the poem's third line "Bridging the slender difference of two stars," the more I thought that Hopkins had a particular comet in mind, and most likely a comet he had personally observed. At first I believed the description to apply to Donati's comet, for when it was first discovered it was not far from the faint star Epsilon Leonis, moving slowly toward nearby 13 Leonis. But the line implies a comet stretching between two stars, not one appearing to move from one star to a neighboring one. Moreover, Epsilon Leonis is more than sixteen times brighter (about three magnitudes) than 13 Leonis. I could find no evidence that this early path of Donati's comet reached England's popular press of the time, and Hopkins might not have known of its early journey.

At first, Comet Tempel, since it passed from view so quickly, seemed to be an unlikely prospect for Hopkins's thought. It was an intrinsically small comet that became conspicuous only because it passed close to Earth. (When larger Comet Hyakutake passed as close in 1996, it was quite bright and sported a tail that stretched halfway across the sky.) The 1864 comet was brighter than second magnitude for only two days, during which time it matched the sky's brighter stars. Yet, while I was searching through newspaper microfilm archives at Queen's University's Douglas library, I found this intriguing article in the London *Times*, the paper's first announcement of the comet:

> The comet first observed on the 5th inst [July] is now distinctly visible to the naked eye in the constellation Taurus and will become each night a more conspicuous object, its approach to the earth being very rapid... On Monday night it will be situate [sic] about five degrees to the left of the Pleiades, passing thence between the stars Iota in Auriga and Beta in Taurus, towards Theta in Gemini, near which it will probably be observed on the morning of August 7. The intensity of light towards the end of the week is from 15 to 20 times greater than during our observations this morning, so that it might be expected to attain the brightness of stars between the first and second magnitude..."[105]

It often happens that a discovery deep in the seeming abyss of a library is as exciting as a find in the depths of space. Finding this small letter in the *Times*, with its reference to the two stars, was as thrilling for me as detecting a new comet. When I mentioned my work to Joseph Ashbrook, then editor of *Sky and Telescope* magazine, he prepared an ephemeris that confirmed the *Times*'s announcement that, shortly after August 1 (the "Monday night" in the extract), the comet passed between Iota Aurigae and Beta Tauri. Even though the stars' Greek letter designations indicated different brightnesses, these two particular stars had similar magnitudes. If the comet's tail followed cometary theory and pointed away from the Sun, then Hopkins might well have seen the comet and its tail "bridge the slender difference" of the two stars.

The next two lines of the poem suggest that in Renaissance thinking, the comet could have "come out of space" or have been "suddenly engender'd by heady elements" in the Earth's atmosphere. The play of which this poem was a part was set in that early time, and the idea that "no man knows" whether comets come from space would have been true then. By the Victorian age, it was common public knowledge, as seen in the many news stories that appeared at the time of the Great Comet of 1861, that comets were not formed from Earth's atmosphere. This major step forward was by Tycho Brahe, who demonstrated that a comet was more distant than the Moon, and later by Edmond Halley, as we have seen in chapter 3. An article in the *London Review*, appearing some four years before the poem, pointed out that the idea of comets coming from the air was proposed originally by Aristotle, and that the idea was accepted well into the Renaissance:

> Aristotle maintained that 'comets' were nothing more than 'meteors generated in the upper regions of the atmosphere.' Seneca conceived they were real stars, but that their appearance was indicative of important changes in the affairs of mankind. 'For six months,' he says in his book *Naturalium Questionum*, 'was this comet to be seen by us, in the happy beginning of the reign of Nero...'

> The comet, in the estimation of the ancients, was beyond all other things in their regard, a political star. It was 'the star of kings, emperors, and rulers; it indicated a destiny to them, and through them was supposed to affect the condition of the people over whom they presided as sovereigns.'[106]

This was a time when comets were known for what they meant rather than for what they were. Lucius Annaeus Seneca had a highly personal stake in trying to attribute comets to the good graces of his patron Nero: he was Nero's tutor when, at age 17, Nero became emperor of Rome. During the first years of Nero's reign, Seneca had considerable power in the government, but when Nero murdered his mother, Agrippina, in the year 59, he coerced Seneca into excusing this heinous act. For the sake of his own survival, Seneca was desperate to interpret the summer comet of the following year as a good omen for Rome's ruler. Seneca spent the last years of his life with his friend Burrus, trying to limit the excesses of Nero's madness. In the year 63, Burrus died and Seneca tried to resign from politics, but Nero, feigning respect for the scientist-philosopher, refused his resignation.

Seneca knew his end under Nero's tyranny was near, and he even abandoned

He his fabric of the Heavens
Hath left to their disputes—perhaps to move
His laughter at their quaint opinions wide
Hereafter, when they come to model heaven
And calculate the stars; how they will wield
The mighty frame; how build, unbuild, contrive
To save appearances; how gird the sphere
With centric and eccentric scribbled o'er,
Cycle and epicycle, orb in orb...

Milton, *Paradise Lost* U

The large spiral galaxy Messier 88, photographed by Steve Larson and David Levy.

his wealth to live in poverty in hopes of forestalling Nero's wrath. It didn't work. In AD 65, Nero accused Seneca of participating in a plot against him and ordered the scholar to "prepare for death." According to custom, this gave Seneca his choice of demise. Seneca elected to cut his wrist and then let himself bleed to death, and in this contemptible fashion the life of one of cometary astronomy's greatest scholars ended.

Centuries later, long after comets were known to travel in orbits about the Sun, politics claimed the life of another cometary scientist and threatened the career of Charles Messier, the first comet hunter. Having discovered several comets, the French astronomer was famous as a gentleman scientist: Louis XV called him the ferret of comets, and he was supported by a pension from his friend, President Jean Baptiste de Saron, of the Paris parliament. De Saron was a man versed in comet orbit calculation, as well as in politics.

But with the onset of the French Revolution, Messier was forced to leave the observatory in Paris. In the evening of September 27, 1793, Messier found a comet in Ophiuchus. As he had done so many times before, he informed his friend de Saron, who attempted to calculate an orbit using the positions Messier supplied. The comet was visible only briefly before it sank into the evening twilight.

However, by this time, de Saron was no longer president of the Paris Parliament. Accused as an enemy of reform, he was in prison awaiting execution by "Madame Guillotine," that creature of the Revolution. It is hard to imagine how de Saron could have cared about comet orbits when he was about to forfeit his head, but he did manage to calculate, from his prison cell, an orbit for Messier's comet. If de Saron's orbit was correct, the comet would move closer to the Sun, then swing away and reappear in the morning sky. On December 29, Messier searched the eastern sky and found his comet close to the position de Saron had predicted for it. Messier wrote of de Saron's last success and hid his note in a newspaper, which he was able to smuggle to the prisoner. On April 20, 1794, just three months before the end of Robespierre's Reign of Terror, de Saron was guillotined. Although Messier survived, his pension was gone, and the acclaimed astronomer was virtually penniless.

Seventy years after Messier's friend died, Hopkins wrote his lines about the journey of a comet that brightens as it sights the Sun. Three comets Hopkins might have seen—Donati's of 1858, Tebutt's of 1861, and Swift-Tuttle of 1862—displayed fine inner condensations that resembled a central star shaking its cocooning mists. But the "central star" of the 1861 comet was described in this way by John Challis in the London *Times* of July 3, 1861:

> The large comet which has so suddenly made its appearance in the
> northern sky was seen here for the first time about 10 o'clock on the
> night of June 30… At midnight the tail reached to within a few
> degrees of the pole-star, and was at least 30 degrees long. The nucleus
> [actually the innermost part of the comet's head] is as bright as a star
> of the first magnitude. In the telescope the coma about the nucleus
> presents the singular appearance of four curved branches.[107]

While the "star of the first magnitude" matches the image evoked in

Hopkins's line, "cocooning mists"—possibly echoing the idea of protective silky threads spun by insect larvae—are common to bright comets and were especially brilliant in the comet heads of 1858, 1861, and 1862. Since the 1864 comet was a smaller object, it had a less brilliant head.

"Shakes its cocooning mists" is a splendid image that aptly depicts the behavior of the comets of 1858 and 1861. Jets of dusty material from the heads of these comets streamed into their tails in periodic eruptions. The comet of 1858 released several gaseous envelopes at irregular intervals, but the 1861 comet shed 11 envelopes of material at the regular rate of one outburst every two days. The comet of 1862 also shook its cocooning mists, but in an unusual way: the material was apparently ejected towards the Sun instead of the more usual direction away from it. Amédeé Guillemin published this report:

> On August 10, 1862, M. Chacornac detected in the head of the comet the presence of a luminous aigrette, a brilliant sector directed towards the sun... New sectors disengaged themselves successively from the nucleus, and on August 26 M. Chacornac determined that between the 10th and the 26th they had succeeded each other to the number of thirteen.[108]

When a comet crosses the plane of the Earth's orbit, sunlight scattered from dust surrounding the comet might cause the appearance of a sunward spike. Comet Arend-Roland, in 1957, and Comet Levy, in 1991, both displayed this unusual feature.

The phrase "Gideon's fleece," in line 11, suggests that a comet absorbs large amounts of light from the Sun, while the space around it is dark, just as the biblical fleece soaks up water while the surrounding ground remains dry:

> *And Gideon said unto God, If thou wilt save Israel by mine hand, as thou hast said, Behold, I will put a fleece of wool in the floor; and if the dew be on the fleece only, and it be dry upon all the Earth beside, then shall I know thou wilt save Israel by mine hand, as thou hast said.*[109]

Sometimes a comet rounds the Sun so quickly that its tail cannot keep up its role of pointing directly away from the Sun. As each dust particle in the tail assumes its own orbit, the comet leaves a tail of particles that curves away from the Sun, rather than shooting straight away from it. When the Comet of 1861 first appeared in the sky over England, it was so bright that it could be seen in daylight. The comet really did appear to "hang upon the flame-cased Sun." (The most recent comet to display this feature was Comet Ikeya-Seki in 1965; its head came within 500,000 kilometers of touching the surface of the Sun.) Comets also have gas tails made of ionized particles that rush out away from the Sun, powered by the pressure of solar radiation we call the solar wind.

By invoking Gideon's fleece, could Hopkins have been speculating about how comets actually shine? In 1864 there was no consensus on whether a comet could soak up light and then re-emit it, or just reflect light from the Sun. In 1877 Amédeé Guillemin wrote that more spectral analysis was needed before one could establish whether comets shine by light other than that reflected by the Sun.[110] But he does include observations made by Father Secchi, who "concluded that, during the first few days, the nucleus shone by its own light, 'perhaps,' the Father observes, 'on account of the incandescent state to which the comet had been brought by its close proximity to the sun.'" Secchi was on the right track; a comet can light up as its gases absorb and then re-emit solar energy like a neon light.

After its close pass by the Earth, the 1864 comet faded. Hopkins uses "tether" —a brilliant choice of words—to describe the Sun's gravitational pull on the comet. A comet is bound to the Sun by a gravitational tether as surely as a dog is bound by its restraining tether. Unlike the dog who can parade about in a circle around a central pole, however, a comet orbits in an ellipse, or a parabola, with the Sun as one of the poles. Hopkins was undoubtedly familiar with the laws of celestial mechanics that Newton first proposed in the seventeenth century. Since the comet of Hopkins's poem was bound by this gravity tether, it faded as it departed from the vicinity of the Sun and the Earth. The phrase "falls off" suggests, however, that the comet was fast receding. And as the comet receded, it shredded, as Hopkins so eloquently put it, its smock of gold. As the Earth passed through the tail of the Comet of 1861, the brilliant comet seemed gold-tinged. This color is rare in a comet, but it was observed on the other occasion during which the Earth is known to have passed through a comet's tail, that of Halley's comet, in 1910.

The fourteenth line of Hopkins's comet poem originally read, "Between the sistering planets," suggesting an image of the fading comet wandering out into the outer solar system.[111] Hopkins substituted the word "Amidst" for "Between," as if to imagine the comet passing planet after planet as it receded from the Sun. We remember that the poem is set in the Renaissance, so the speaker could not have been aware of the 1781 discovery of Uranus and the 1846 finding of Neptune; to Giulia, the poem's speaker, Saturn would have been the farthest planet. The poem's closing lines relate the events of the comet's journey to that of a human life. Giulia is resigned to the end of a fine life and a satisfying relationship; like the comet, she has drawn heat from the Sun.

What may have motivated Hopkins to use the comet analogy in a play set in Renaissance Italy? Besides his fresh memory of the comet of 1864, two earlier items in the contemporary newspapers may have suggested it, one connecting the 1861 comet to Italy and the other invoking the Renaissance:

> Have we not seen quite recently, in 1861, when the great comet of that year appeared, how it was currently reported in Italy, and doubtless elsewhere, that the new star was a sign of the speedy return of Francis II and his restoration to the throne of the Two Sicilies; and also that it presaged the fall of the temporal power and the death of Pope Pius IX? 'We ought not to be astonished at the persistence of these superstitions, which only the spread of science can annihilate for ever.'[112]

The second newspaper item concerned a debate at the Academy of Sciences about the "terrifying" comet of 1556, which is said to have been a cause of the abdication of Charles V of Spain. With the possible exception of Genghis Khan, Charles was the Hapsburg Emperor who ruled perhaps more territories than anyone else. He retired of his own will around 1556, living quietly on his estate and indulging his interest in clocks, and died two years later. Charles's comet appeared in the southern sky of 1556, moving through Corvus and Virgo. In 1751, scientist Richard Dunthorne suggested that it was the same comet "that created astonishment throughout Europe" in 1264.[113] Dunthorne went on to prophesy a return in 1848; in 1857, with Charles's comet still unseen, J. Russell Hind, at that time one of England's best known astronomers, refined that forecast to August of either 1858 or 1860.

Even in Hind's day, astronomers understood that the gravitational pulls of the planets can affect the period of a comet as it travels about the Sun. Hind wrote in 1859:

> If a comet experienced no resistance while performing its journey round that luminary, it would make its appearance after equal intervals of time... But the movements of comets are greatly disturbed by the attraction of the various planets belonging to the solar system, particularly by Jupiter and Saturn, which far exceed the rest in magnitude.[114]

Both the *Times* of July 4, 1861, and the *Illustrated London News*, two days later, printed these same words:

> ...the comet gave rise to an animated discussion at yesterday's sitting of the Academy of Sciences... M. Babinet remarked that M. Hind's Ephemerides of Charles V's comet gave it the precise position of the present one. [This means that by calculating the future course of the comet that appeared in 1556, it would appear in the same place that the Comet of 1861 now appears.] M. Bromine had predicted its return in 1858, and M. Hind admitted that it might return between 1856 and 1860... If this were so, the present comet was the same that had been observed in 1556, and caused the abdication of Charles V... M. Leverrier was not of M. Babinet's opinion. M. Hind's table showed different positions which Charles V's comet might occupy in the event of its return, and the question was so undetermined that it was no wonder to find a position in the table answering to that of the present comet... [The] motion of the present comet...was so different from that given in the table, that the identity of the two comets could no longer be admitted."[115]

The scientists in this debate were well known. Most of the letters to the *Times* concerning the Comet of 1861 came from Hind, who was director of the Observatory in Regent's Park, London, and had written a short book about the Comet of 1556.[116] Leverrier made calculations which led to the discovery of

Neptune in 1846.

Although *I am like a slip of comet* was Hopkins's only comet poem, his interest in comets lasted throughout his life. In 1874, he observed Coggia's comet: "The comet," he wrote in his Journal, "I have seen it at bedtime in the west, with head to the ground, white, a soft, well-shaped tail, not big: I felt a certain awe and instress, a feeling of strangeness, flight (it hangs like a shuttlecock at the height, before it falls)…"[117]

The lively image of a shuttlecock implies an object that should be in motion but which, at that second, is not moving. The comet, like the shuttlecock, appeared about to plunge down toward the horizon. Used in badminton, a shuttlecock is fitted with a ring of feathers that resembles the soft, wide tail of Coggia's comet. Note also how Hopkins is reacting to the comet's inscape through his feeling of "awe and instress."

Not long after this comet appearance, Hopkins wrote to his mother from North Wales about a possible comet discovery. No longer at Stonyhurst, Hopkins could not discuss his observation with an astronomer: "I have seen one three nights…in Cancer. It is small and pale but quite visible. If it is not a comet then it must be a nebula and then it is strange I should not have noticed it before… At ten o'clock it is well visible in the northeast, not high; later it would be higher."[118]

This object turned out to be not a comet but the Beehive or Praesepe Cluster. Charles Messier himself included the Beehive as No. 44 in his famous list of objects that could be confused with new comets. Although Messier knew that M44 was not a comet, Hopkins should be forgiven this interesting error. When the Beehive is low in the sky, it tends to hide its true identity of a cluster of several hundred distant stars, masquerading instead as a nebulous object, or even as a comet. In December, 1878, when the letter was written, the cluster would have been rising before dawn after several months of invisibility; Hopkins might have forgotten it from the year before. In a subsequent letter he admitted his mistake: "What I took for a comet (do you remember?) turned out to be a well known nebula of great size. Praesepe it is called, in Cancer."[119]

Hopkins's last written reference to comets appears in an 1883 letter to his friend and fellow-poet Coventry Patmore, who had included this passage in *Wedding Sermon*:

To move
Frantic, like comets to our bliss,
Forgetting that we always miss,
And so to seek and fly the sun,
By turns, around which love should run…[120]

Patmore's point seems to be that comets never get so close to the Sun that they are swallowed by it. Hopkins was confused by his poetic style. He thought that Patmore's image was "a contrast between the long elliptic orbits of comets, with the sun almost at one end, and the short ones, practically circles, of the planets, with the sun at the center."[121] Hopkins went on to suggest that "it might be clearer." It is true that the perihelia, or closest points to the Sun, of most comet orbits are far enough from the Sun that they do not collide. However, there is a group of comets, the Kreutz sungrazers, that might constitute a counterpoint to Patmore's idea. Sungrazing comets are exceptional because they whip around the Sun at less than one million miles from its fiery surface. First studied in detail as a single group with a possible common origin by Heinrich Kreutz in 1888, these comets share a similar orbit. In the 1980s, the Solwind and Solar Maximum mission satellites detected a series of Kreutz sungrazers actually colliding with the Sun. The grandeur of these comets depends on the time of year they round the Sun. Comet Pereyra, at perihelion in 1963, was bright but far from spectacular. But the Great Comets of 1882 and 1965 rounded the Sun not far from the September equinox, squeaking past the Sun at a distance of less than 300,000 miles and putting on splendid shows. These two comets almost certainly last brushed the Sun as a single object, perhaps as the Great Comet of 1106.[122]

From his poems, letters, and journal writings, it is apparent that Hopkins's vigorous interest in observing the night sky profoundly affected his poetry. The detail of the astronomical imagery in *I am like a slip of comet* shows a conciseness and accuracy that befits a watcher of the sky. Hopkins's keen observational skill, coupled with his great imaginative power, added a special dimension to his writings and also to the astronomical tradition that continues to enrich the world of English poetry.

CHAPTER VI

Dark Sky
from Walden Pond

Independence Day, 1845: far from the reveling hordes in Boston, a 28-year-old maverick called Henry David Thoreau was trying to bring the theme of independence to a different level. For a true freedom of the mind, the young writer believed in simplifying his life by learning the lessons of Nature. It is a familiar goal to many of us. We can picture a quiet lake on a sunny afternoon, a cottage with smoke wafting through a chimney, perhaps even someone setting up a small telescope at lakeside in anticipation of a starry night. We may even try to relate a bee hovering over a flowering plant, or the appearance of the Moon in the late afternoon sky, to our own experience, just as Gerard Manley Hopkins did through his inscape, and just as Thoreau tried to do in his writing.

Born in 1817, Henry David Thoreau lived his 44 short years in Concord, a small community near a pond west of Boston. Educated at Harvard, Thoreau had a highly independent streak. When his friend, Ralph Waldo Emerson, bragged of how a Harvard education covers all the branches of learning, Thoreau quipped, "All the branches, yes, but none of the roots!"

Thoreau's first book, *A Week on the Concord and Merrimack Rivers*, was well received by critics but sold so poorly that the publisher delivered all the unsold copies—some 700 out of a print run of 1000—to the writer's home. "I now have a library of nearly nine hundred volumes," he wrote, "over seven hundred of which I wrote myself."[123] It was only near his death that Thoreau learned that his writings were becoming more popular. His final illness began after he refused to cancel a lecture appearance when he was suffering from a cold. The cold worsened into a bad attack of bronchitis and finally mushroomed into acute tuberculosis, from which he died in 1862. Although Thoreau is recognized as one of the best of American writers, he actually left us only two well-known works. One of

Henry David Thoreau

them, an essay called *Civil Disobedience*, became the model for the careers of two of the leaders of our century, Mahatma Gandhi and Martin Luther King. *Walden*, which can be called a prose poem, is Thoreau's other celebrated work. On the surface, *Walden* is about a writer's experience that began on July 4, 1845, when Thoreau went to live on the shore of Walden Pond near Concord. Even in the mid-19th century, Thoreau's home was not terribly removed from civilization. Less than half a mile from the road leading to Concord, the location allowed Thoreau to walk to town several times a week. He wanted to demonstrate that by simplifying the details of life, it was possible to live happily without complex possessions. The fact that Thoreau took some seven years to turn Walden, the experiment, into *Walden*, the book, shows that the book is far more than an account of a year of the writer's life.

"I went to the woods," he writes in the profound opening of Walden, "because I wished to live deliberately, to front only the essential facts of life, and see if I could not learn what it had to teach, and not, when I came to die, discover that I had not lived." Thoreau lived in his cabin at Walden for a little over two years, with at least one interruption for a trip to the woods in Maine, and another in 1846, to spend a night in Concord Jail for refusing to pay a poll tax.

Although his years at Walden are what he is most famous for, Thoreau tried to live his entire life as modestly as possible, relating even the austerity of the night sky to his ideals. To be different merely for the sake of being different, however, was not Thoreau's way. The seed of Thoreau's convictions came from his close friendship with Ralph Waldo Emerson, one of America's most famous writers, whose philosophy included both a closeness with nature, and a truthfulness with oneself. Emerson's essay, titled *Self Reliance*, preached a solidarity with oneself:

The first in time and the first in importance of the influences of the mind

*is that of nature. Every day, the sun; and, after sunset, Night and her
stars. Ever the winds blow; ever the grass grows. Every day, men and
women, conversing—beholding and beholden. The scholar is he of all men
whom this spectacle most engages. He must settle its value in his mind.
What is nature to him? There is never a beginning, there is never an end,
to the inexplicable continuity of this web of God, but always circular
power returning into itself... The astronomer discovers that geometry, a
pure abstraction of the human mind, is the measure of planetary motion.
The chemist finds proportions and intelligible method throughout matter;
and science is nothing but the finding of analogy, identity, in the most
remote parts.*[124]

The other key, to be true to oneself, is an idea that remains strong in the
American consciousness:

*A foolish consistency is the hobgoblin of little minds, adored by little states-
men and philosophers and divines. With consistency a great soul has
simply nothing to do. He may as well concern himself with his shadow on
the wall. Speak what you think now in hard words and to-morrow speak
what to-morrow thinks in hard words again, though it contradict
everything you said to-day. 'Ah, so you shall be sure to be misunderstood.'
Is it so bad then to be misunderstood? Pythagoras was misunderstood, and
Socrates, and Jesus, and Luther, and Copernicus, and Galileo, and
Newton, and every pure and wise spirit that ever took flesh. To be great is
to be misunderstood.*[125]

THOREAU AND THE SKY

"I just looked up at a fine twinkling star," an undated entry from Thoreau's journal from the 1840s says, "and thought that a voyager whom I know, now many
days sail from this coast, might possibly be looking up at that same star with
me."[126] During one week in 1994, as we shall see in chapter 7, this thought
proved literally true, as virtually every telescope on Earth peered at the planet

Jupiter. Thoreau's thought later appears in expanded form, as he launches into the diverse but related subjects of space and time: "We might try our lives by a thousand simple tests," he wrote at the opening of *Walden*, "as, for instance, that the same sun that ripens my beans illumines at once a system of earths like ours." Out into space but not into time: "What distant and different beings in the various mansions of the universe are contemplating the same one at the same moment!... Could a greater miracle take place than for us to look through each other's eyes for an instant?" And in the very next sentence, he travels first into time but not space, and next into both space and time: "We should live in all the ages of the world for an hour; ay, in all the worlds of the ages. I know of no reading of another's experience so startling and informing as this would be."[127]

Although Thoreau's published essays and books are his most famous pieces, some of his best writing appeared in his journals, which he kept for many years. While writing in a book requires drafting and careful thought, a journal allows an unfettered, spontaneous look at life, and in Thoreau's hand the journals show some of his most interesting thoughts. He would write in his cabin, or while walking. When he forgot his paper he would write on birch bark. I can't remember the number of times that humid nights have made the electric wires sizzle and almost cry out in my own, late twentieth-century nights. More than a century ago, Thoreau noted the same thing, as he wrote on September 12, 1851: "I heard the telegraph wire vibrating like an aeolian harp." On the twilight evening of June 15, 1852, Thoreau wrote: "It is candle-light. The fishes leap. The meadows sparkle with the coppery light of fireflies. The evening star, multiplied by undulating water, is like bright sparks of fire continually ascending." This evening star, subject of so many great poems, was in fact Venus that night. Earth's sister planet was in Cancer, shining at minus 4.5 magnitude, virtually as bright as it ever gets.[128] But Thoreau does not limit his description to its effect in the sky. The planet's reflection in the gently rolling waters of Walden pond offers a dramatic addition to what the sky already shows. And as the pond quiets down during the night, it reflects the images from fainter and fainter stars.

At our family cottage at Jarnac Pond in the Québec woods, I have seen the faint fourth magnitude stars of the Little Dipper reflected in the still, mirror-like waters of the pond late at night. In any event, it is being outdoors instead of in, under the night sky instead of asleep in bed, that results in unique discoveries like planets reflecting off water: "It would be well perhaps if we were to spend more of our days and nights without any obstruction between us and the celestial bodies, if the poet did not speak so much from under a roof, or the saint dwell there so long."

Had Thoreau used a telescope that night, he would have observed Venus in its dramatic crescent phase. But it was as much a part of his purpose to inscape, as Hopkins might have said, the full impact of Venus—pond and all—without using any optical aid. *Simplify* was his clarion call: he writes proudly in *Walden*'s opening chapter that he built his entire home for $28.12 1/2, an enviably low price; in 1996 my fiancé Wendee and I spent $150,000 for our home and $6,000 more for an observatory to get as good a feel of the night sky as Thoreau had.

A feel for the sky was an important part of what Thoreau got out of Walden. On one sparkling night, for example, he found he was much closer to the skies than he was to his colleagues. He wrote in Walden:

> Both place and time were changed and I dwelt nearer to those parts of the universe and to those eras of history which had most attracted me. Where I lived was as far off as many a region viewed nightly by astronomers. We are wont to imagine rare and delectable places in some remote and more celestial corner of the system, behind the constellation of Cassiopeia's Chair, far from noise and disturbance. I discovered that my house actually had its site in such a withdrawn, but forever new and unprofaned, part of the universe. If it were worth the while to settle in those parts near to the Pleiades or the Hyades, or to Aldebaran or Altair, then I was really there, or at an equal remoteness from the life which I had left behind.[129]

THOREAU'S VIEW OF SCIENCE

Although Thoreau was quite at home with the ecosystem around his Walden home, and knew the stars and constellations well, his writings almost shunned this knowledge in favor of something more spiritual. "When I consider how, after sunset, the stars come out gradually in troops from behind the hills and woods," he wrote in his journal in 1840, "I confess that I could not have contrived a more curious and inspiring sight."[130] Curious and inspiring are two words that lead to the heart of Thoreau's concept of what the sky and its contents mean. The sky is inspiring because its vastness of time and place compels him to look inward, and, though he was as curious about the sky above as he was about the ecosystem at his Walden home, his transcendentalist philosophy dissuaded him from interpreting its physical nature. In his journals and *Walden*, Thoreau almost delights in scorning the method of science, in which objects and phenomena are observed and interpreted. An unusual thing or event, in and of itself, did not capture Thoreau's attention. For example, in the spring of 1854 he flatly refused the offer of a two-headed calf from a farmer who thought he would want to study such a freak birth from one of his cows. Thoreau's interest in nature seemed essentially a springboard to a greater understanding of self: "I am not interested in mere phenomena, though it were the explosion of a planet, only as it may have lain in the experience of a human being."[131]

> I must walk more with free senses. It is as bad to study stars and clouds as flowers and stones. I must let my senses wander as my thoughts, my eyes see without looking. Carlyle said that how to observe was to look, but I say that it is rather to see, and the more you look the less you will observe. I have the habit of attention to much excess that my senses get no rest, but suffer from a constant strain. Be not preoccupied with looking. Go not to the object; let it come to you.[132]

This concept of seeing is more of a totality of observation rather than an occasional attempt at looking. William Herschel, the famed British Astronomer Royal, felt the same way about the skill which led to his discovery of the planet Uranus: "Seeing is in some respects an art which must be learnt. To make a person see with such a power is nearly the same as if I had been asked to make him play one of Handel's fugues upon the organ. Many a night have I been practising to see, and it would be strange if one did not acquire a certain dexterity by such constant practice."[133]

Years later, Herschel expanded the concept of learning to see with one's telescope:

It would be hard to be condemned, because I have tried to improve telescopes and practised continually to see with them. These instruments have played me so many tricks that I have at last found them out in many of their humours and have made them confess to me what they would have concealed, if I had not with such perseverance and patience courted them. I have tortured them with powers, flattered them with attendance to find out the critical moments when they would act, tried them with specula of short or long focus, a large aperture or a narrow one; it would be hard if they had not been kind to me at last.[134]

How does this thought differ from Thoreau's sense of what defines accurate seeing? "What I need is not to look at all," he concludes, "but a true sauntering of the eye."[135] Although Thoreau was never a scientist in the literal sense, and though he even had a disdain for the narrow research areas of some of the scientists of his time, he understood the great power of observation. This power can be aided by a telescope, as it was in Herschel's case, but it does not need a telescope. For Thoreau, the idea is part of a philosophy born from the transcendentalist movement in American literature, of which he, his friend Ralph Waldo Emerson, and Nathaniel Hawthorne were lynchpins. Transcendentalism was a movement that did not flourish long—it was strongest only during the 1830s and 1840s—and it emphasized intuition, rather than knowledge, as a way of learning.

"Color, which is a poet's wealth," Thoreau emphasized in the fall of 1852, "is so expensive that most take to mere outline or pencil sketches and become men of science."[136] A week later he added, "It is impossible for the same person to see things from the poet's point of view and that of the man of science. The poet's second love may be science, not his first—when use has worn off the bloom."[137] It would seem that Thoreau's vision is completely at odds with that of this book, but it is not. In its strictest sense, the scientific method, as we discussed in chapter one, does not allow for intuition, dreaming, or excitement. But in reality science is practiced by people with imagination, humor, and varying ways of looking at nature, and there are countless cases of scientific discoveries coming out of other than official channels of research. A Japanese amateur astronomer equipped with a large pair of binoculars, for example, discovered the great comet of 1996 in time to allow professional astronomers to plan observing the rare spectacle. This was true even in Thoreau's time: the hexagonal ring-shaped chemical structure of the benzene ring, for example, came to the mind of discoverer Friedrich Kekulé in 1865 out of a dream.

I do not believe that Thoreau was showing disdain for science, but rather for what he sees as the confined way in which science was being practised. Just as I am, in this book, trying to see the poetry in science, Thoreau dared to relate the events and objects of natural science, such as his view of Venus reflected in Walden's waters, to his own world view. Science is much more complicated now than it was in Thoreau's time, and maybe that is a good reason for us to see it in a wider sense than did Thoreau a century and a half ago.

That scientists do not have a monopoly on science is hardly a new idea. A child's first view of the heavens under a dark sky inspires a sense of wonder and awe, and the child's first longing is not for facts and answers but for a relationship: what does that sky have to do with me? Where do I fit in? Even for many scientists, this wonder never leaves, and in poetry the wonder appears again and again. Fifty years after Thoreau died, Walt Whitman wrote of the great divide between scientific theory and simple wonder:

> *When I heard the learn'd astronomer,*
> *When the proofs, the figures, were ranged in columns before me,*
> *When I was shown the charts and diagrams, to add, divide, and measure*
> *them,*
> *When I sitting heard the astronomer lecture with much applause in the*
> *lecture-room,*
> *How soon unaccountable I became tired and sick,*
> *Till rising and gliding out I wander'd off by myself,*
> *In the mystical moist night-air, and from time to time,*
> *Look'd up in perfect silence at the stars.*[138]

Magical thoughts such as these will not lead to an increased awareness of the ages of the stars, the nature of the Whirlpool Galaxy, or the thickness of Saturn's rings. But one doesn't need to know these things in order to sense the magic, and, beyond a very simple level, factual knowledge is not needed to appreciate the silence of the stars of Walt Whitman, nor is it needed to relate to Thoreau's transcendentalist aim. *Walden* is that rare literary form called a prose poem, and Thoreau was a poet in the ancient sense of a prophet or seer. The poet, he wrote, was not necessarily a writer of rhyme, but was "the toughest son of earth and of Heaven," able to see a higher power in nature, a force which a scientist might miss. The poet's sky was not an encyclopedia but a tabernacle.

In a sense, Thoreau's wisdom can help solve some modern-day scientific controversies. One recent debate, for example, concerns the status of Pluto, that cold and distant world. The question is, should we call Pluto a planet or an asteroid? Nature does not distinguish between minor planets and major planets, just as it doesn't differentiate between a hill and a mountain. In his journal, Thoreau agreed that we need to be as unbiased as Nature is: "Not a single scientific term of distinction is distinct to the purpose, for you would fain perceive something, and you must approach the object totally unprejudiced. You must be aware that no thing is what you have taken it to be."[139]

I became an astronomer not to learn the facts about the sky but to feel its majesty. Perhaps skywatchers feel most a part of the infinite cosmic drama when we're with our telescopes, and our friends, at a star party. It's late, it's dark, it's clear, the Milky Way arches overhead, and we know we're where we want to be. Although it consists of many parts, the night sky as a whole is both familiar and ever-changing. In the fall of 1852 Thoreau wrote:

> After whatever revolutions in my moods and experiences, when I come forth at evening, as if from years of confinement to the house, I see the few stars which make the constellation of the Lesser Bear in the same relative position—the everlasting geometry of the stars. How incredible to be described are these bright points which appear in the blue sky as darkness increases, said to be other worlds, like the berries on the hills when the summer is ripe! ... Far in this ethereal sea lie the Hesperian isles, unseen by day, but when the darkness comes their fires are seen from this shore, as Columbus saw the fires of San Salvador."[140]

The Hesperian Isles beckon all of us. According to one interpretation, they were the daughters of Hesperus, the most splendid star in the sky. We know from Tennyson (see chapter 4) that Hesper is the name given to Venus when that planet is in the evening sky. The daughters lived in a garden at the extreme western end of the world, and guarded the celestial flock of night. The daughters defend their secrets well; no matter how much we learn, it is not possible to know everything about the sky. The islands are magnificent: Milton describes them as "a heaven on earth,"[141] and he adds:

Groves whose rich trees wept odorous gums and balm,
Others whose fruit burnished with golden rind
Hung amiable, Hesperian fables true,
If true, here only.[142]
...Now glow'd the firmament
With living sapphires: Hesperus, that led
The starry host, rode brightest, till the Moon,
Rising in clouded majesty, at length
Apparent queen, unveil'd her peerless light,
And o'er the dark her silver mantle threw.[143]

These are powerful islands, uniting princes, poets, and stargazers who search for something better, something transcendent, out of life. Thoreau invokes the sun as I hoped in much the same grand style of other writers of the time, but it is Tennyson who makes it personal in a poem that speaks powerfully to all of us who wish to find their dreams reflected in the western sky:

The lights begin to twinkle from the rocks;
The long day wanes; the slow moon climbs; the deep
Moans round with many voices. Come, my friends,
'Tis not too late to seek a newer world.
Push off, and sitting well in order smite
The sounding furrows; for my purpose holds
To sail beyond the sunset, and the baths
Of all the western stars, until I die.
It may be that the gulfs will wash us down;

It may be we shall touch the Happy Isles,
And see the great Achilles, whom we knew.
Tho' much is taken, much abides; and tho'
We are not now that strength which in old days
Moved earth and heaven; that which we are, we are;
One equal temper of heroic hearts,
Made weak by time and fate, but strong in will
To strive, to seek, to find, and not to yield.[144]

For a skywatcher, to visit the Hesperian Isles is to understand the precious beauty of the night. Like the idyllic lakeside cottage we dreamt of at the start of this chapter, the isles herald a night of stars, galaxies, and serenity. And if we choose to augment that feeling with knowledge and experience, then our appreciation will increase as nights pass. "Only that day dawns to which we are awake," is *Walden*'s closing thought. "The Sun is but a morning star."

Wake! For the Sun, who scatter'd into flight
The Stars before him from the Field of Night,
*   Drives Night along with them from Heav'n, and strikes*
The Sultán's Turret with a Shaft of Light.

Before the phantom of False morning died,
Methought a Voice within the Tavern cried,
*   "When all the Temple is prepared within,*
Why nods the drowsy Worshipper outside?"

Edward FitzGerald, *The Rubáiyát of Omar Khayyám of Naishápúr*, reworked from the work of Omar, a twelfth-century Persian astronomer and poet.[V]

The crescent moon and Venus. Photo by Roy Bishop.

CHAPTER VII

A Terrible Beauty is Born: When Science Becomes Poetry

Turning and turning in the widening gyre
The falcon cannot hear the falconer;
Things fall apart; the center cannot hold;
Mere anarchy is loosed upon the world,
The blood-dimmed tide is loosed, and everywhere
The ceremony of innocence is drowned;
The best lack all conviction, while the worst
Are full of passionate intensity.

Surely some revelation is at hand;
Surely the Second Coming is at hand.
The Second Coming! Hardly are those words out
When a vast image out of Spiritus Mundi
Troubles my sight: somewhere in sands of the desert
A shape with lion body and the head of a man,
A gaze blank and pitiless as the sun,
Is moving its slow thighs, while all about it
Reel shadows of the indignant desert birds.
The darkness drops again; but now I know
That twenty centuries of stony sleep
Were vexed to nightmare by a rocking cradle,

And what rough beast, its hour come round at last,
Slouches towards Bethlehem to be born?

W.B. Yeats, *The Second Coming*, 1920[145]

Over the years the dual magnets in astronomy and literature have pulled my interest, and I've tried to bring these two pursuits together. By far the best such effort did not come from me, but from Nature herself. In 1994, twenty-one fragments of the shattered comet Shoemaker-Levy 9 collided with Jupiter in the mightiest collision ever seen in our solar system.

We are all in the gutter, but some of us are looking at the stars.

Oscar Wilde, *Lady Windermere's Fan* (1891) Act III [W]

Comet Levy (1990c) became a conspicuous object during the summer of 1990. Photo by David Levy

The story of Shoemaker-Levy 9 began some 4.5 billion years ago, when a comet slowly formed out of the dust and ice in the outer part of the infant solar system. The comet spent eons as part of a sphere of comets we call the Oort cloud. For some reason—possibly the passage of a nearby star—the comet left the distant cloud and began to travel toward the inner part of the solar system. Over several orbits it passed close to the planet Jupiter. Around 1929, the same year as another historical crash here on Earth, the comet approached Jupiter in such a way that its orbit was altered. Instead of circling the Sun directly, the comet was now moving around Jupiter as a satellite.

My part of the story began one summer afternoon in 1960, when my uncle gave me my first telescope. The night that followed was pivotal. My parents and I set up the black-tubed telescope, which we named Echo after the communications satellite, in our back yard. Having no star chart, I set Echo on the brightest star in the sky. That was no star, it turned out: the four small moons that accompanied it made me certain I was looking at Jupiter.

I did not know then, nor did anyone else, that an additional moon was orbiting Jupiter that night. It was Comet Shoemaker-Levy 9. But unlike the large moons which travel in near circular orbits in regular periods, the comet cruised along a strange road that brought it to some distance from Jupiter, then sent it rushing headlong towards the planet. By 1970, I was well along in my search for comets, a calling I knew would take up many night hours, and one which might never be successful. At the time I was an undergraduate student in Acadia University's English Department, and there I found, from the pen of a long-dead writer, the justification for the road I soon took. The writer was Thoreau, and his words seemed directed at my vision:

> *I learned this, at least, by my experiment: that if one advances confidently in the direction of his dreams, and endeavors to live the life he has imagined, then he will meet with a success unexpected in common hours...*

> *If a man does not keep pace with his companions, perhaps it is because he hears a different drummer. Let him step to the music which he hears, however measured or far away.*[146]

At virtually the same time I read Thoreau's words, Comet Shoemaker-Levy 9 was passing closer to Jupiter than it ever had before, so close that it almost broke apart from the giant planet's gravity. In 1984, after searching for 19 years, I finally discovered my first comet, and a few years later I joined the team of Eugene and Carolyn Shoemaker. For seven nights each month, we used the 18-inch diameter telescope at Palomar Observatory to search for comets and asteroids. Throughout the first years we spent at this telescope, our comet, still unknown to anyone, continued to orbit Jupiter, and on July 7, 1992, it headed toward the giant planet in its closest approach yet. As the comet skimmed just 70,000 kilometers from Jupiter's cloud tops, the planet's gravity stressed the comet some two hundred times more strongly than the Moon pulls on Earth's oceans:

> *It is the very error of the moon;*
> *She comes more near the earth than she was wont,*
> *And makes men mad.*

> Shakespeare, *Othello*[147]

On one side lay the ocean, and on one
Lay a great water, and the moon was full.

Alfred, Lord Tennyson, *Morte d'Arthur*, 1842[148]

"And the moon was full,"
As the poet said
And I aptly quoted.
And its being full
And right overhead,
Small but strong and round,
By its tidal pull
Made all being full.

Robert Frost, *Kitty Hawk*, 1962[149]

So strongly did Jupiter pull on the comet that the small body began to break apart. Within two hours, what once was a single comet was now a string of 12 comets, stretching some vast distance. No one on Earth knew of the sensational opening act of the comet's final performance.

DISCOVERY

The year 1993 began badly for the Shoemakers and me at Palomar Mountain Observatory. We were scheduled to observe the sky for seven nights in January, in the hope that at least four would be clear, yet we got only one clear night. February was even worse; of the seven nights, we had only one clear hour. During this time we prepared several dozen pieces of film for use and stored them in a light-tight box. Unknown to us, someone opened the box during the time between our February and our March observing periods, and exposed the film to light.

The March observing run began well under a sparkling clear sky, but we quickly discovered that our film was useless. However, we had stored the film so that the topmost films protected the lower ones, and we were able to limp through that first night using the partially damaged films. The second night began with a fresh supply of film, but after a few hours the sky began to cloud over. As we stood outdoors looking at the sky, I suggested that we continue observing despite the weather, since the forecast was not favorable. Gene reminded me that, since we spent some four dollars each time we put a film into the telescope, which adds up to several thousand dollars a year on film, we could not afford to waste film under less than clear conditions. It was Gene's finance-based argument that led me to suggest a solution: why not use the damaged films, of which we had perhaps a dozen left? This way, we would continue to observe and waste nothing but our own time.

So it was that on March 23, 1993, I took two photographs of a region in Virgo in a partly clouded sky, on damaged films, using a telescope almost 60 years old. Jupiter was in the telescope's field of view. Two days later, Carolyn completed scanning all the films except for the last ones, and she inserted the two Jupiter films into her stereomicroscope. By scanning both films at once, in stereo, Carolyn would see the identical fields as though they were a single photograph. However, any object moving would appear to float atop the starry background. This was an elegant way of searching for comets.

It had been so long, though, since Carolyn had found anything that whenever she would adjust her chair, or clear her throat, Gene and I would look up expectantly. We did that when, just after four o'clock on the afternoon of March 25, Carolyn suddenly tensed and sat up straight in her chair. "I don't know what this is," she announced, "but it looks like a squashed comet." Gene and I took turns looking at the strangest object we had ever seen in the stereomicroscope.

In our discovery message, we wrote: "The image is most unusual in that it appears as a dense, linear bar very close to 1 arcminute long, oriented roughly east-west. No central condensation [a thickening of the comet near its center] is observable in either of the two images. A fainter, wispy 'tail' extends north of the bar and to the west."[150]

Before the comet could be announced and named, it needed to be confirmed by an independent observation. I telephoned Jim Scotti, a close friend and fellow astronomer who was observing with a larger telescope than ours from a site four hundred miles to the east of us. Skeptical at first, Jim finally agreed to turn his telescope to the coordinates I provided. Two hours later, when I called again,

Jim was virtually speechless. "I am trying to pick my jaw off the floor," he said. As he described the comet's appearance—several distinct heads, each with its own tail, and two large wings of dust—I repeated each phrase to the others. In the background during this magical time, our cassette recorder happened to be playing the exultant fourth movement of Beethoven's First Symphony.

We thought that comet, eventually named Shoemaker-Levy 9, had given us its best performance just from its appearance at discovery. We were wrong. Images taken with large telescopes revealed that the comet was now split into 21 fragments, stretched out, one astronomer wrote, like pearls on a string. And like the falcon of Yeats's poem turning and turning in a widening gyre, the comet was orbiting Jupiter in a path that, we soon learned, had caused it to graze the planet months before we found it hurtling away.

On March 25, 1811—coincidentally 182 years to the day before our discovery of Shoemaker-Levy 9—Honoré Flaugergues also discovered a comet. This Great Comet quickly brightened until it could be seen without a telescope, and it remained visible to the naked eye for ten months. By December, the comet had a tail more than 70 degrees long, covering a significant part of the sky. (Its appearance was even credited with the coincidentally ultra-fine wines from that year.) In

Hung be the heavens with black, yield day to night!
Comets, importing change of times and states,
Brandish your crystal tresses in the sky
And with them scourge the bad revolving stars
That have consented unto Henry's death!
King Henry the Fifth, too famous to live long!
England ne'er lost a king of so much worth.

Shakespeare, *1 Henry VI* [X]

If Shakespeare wrote Henry VI by 1592, these opening lines might hark back to major comet appearances in 1587, 1590, and 1591; a magnificent comet appeared near the North celestial pole in 1593. By no stretch of the imagination could any of these comets have resembled this image of Comet Shoemaker-Levy 9, taken by Jim Scotti on March 30, 1993, less than a week after its discovery.

October, 1816, the English poet John Keats wrote of the thrill of discovering a new work of literature, in this case a lively translation of Homer by George Chapman. Keats stayed up all night with his friend and former schoolteacher reading Homer in Chapman's translation, then he walked home at dawn, wrote the poem, and sent it to his teacher by 10 a.m. mail that same day. Most critics agree that the poet was probably comparing that thrill of discovery to the feeling William Herschel had on his finding of Uranus in 1781, an event that occurred 14 years before Keats was born. I believe that the poet had a different discovery in mind, that of the Comet of 1811, when he penned his famous sonnet *On First Looking into Chapman's Homer*.

Whether the discovery lies between the covers of a book, or on photographic films at an observatory, or in the eyepiece of a telescope, the thrill is the same:

> *Much have I traveled in the realms of gold,*
> *And many goodly states and kingdoms seen;*
> *Round many western islands have I been*
> *Which bards in fealty to Apollo hold.*
> *Oft of one wide expanse had I been told*
> *That deep-brow'd Homer ruled as his demesne;*
> *Yet did I never breathe its pure serene*
> *Till I heard Chapman speak out loud and bold:*
> *Then felt I like some watcher of the skies*
> *When a new planet swims into his ken;*
> *Or like stout Cortez when with eagle eyes*
> *He stared at the Pacific—and all his men*
> *Looked at each other with a wild surmise—*
> *Silent, upon a peak in Darien.*[151]

IMPACT

On May 22, 1993, the Shoemakers and I were again observing at the 18-inch when the announcement came in: Comet Shoemaker-Levy 9, it turned out, was about to fulfill Yeats's prophecy in a strange way. Like the falcon unable to hear its falconer, the comet was skating out of control. Already, things had fallen apart;

the center couldn't hold as the comet was continuing to split apart. Its brightest fragment was breaking up into several pieces. The fragments, we learned that day, would move away from Jupiter until July, then start to approach Jupiter again. In July 1994, the comet would crash into Jupiter. We had 14 months to ponder what "mere anarchy" the comet would unleash on that distant world as it slammed into Jupiter at the unheard of speed of 60 kilometers per second.

As the time to impact week shortened, astronomers prepared their telescopes for observing the event. Clearly this kind of event was so rare that it demanded maximum observing time, on as many telescopes as possible. Almost every major telescope on Earth was poised to watch Jupiter in the most massive observing campaign for a single event since Galileo first turned his telescope to the sky more than 400 years ago. In addition, an armada of spacecraft, including the Hubble Space Telescope and the Galileo space probe, were ready to turn their sights toward Jupiter. When we arrived at the Space Telescope Science Institute in Baltimore, Maryland, on the afternoon of July 16, 1994, we found the place overrun with reporters and broadcasters from all over the world. It was in this tense atmosphere that we awaited the results from Jupiter, where Fragment A of Comet Shoemaker-Levy 9 was hurtling into the atmosphere at more than 130,000 miles per hour. One reporter teased us about how embarrassed we would be if the show turned out to be a dud. We were as concerned as he that as big as the event was, astronomers might not be able to detect any of it from Earth. We had two reasons for this concern. One was that the comet was so small, and Jupiter so large, that no matter how big the comet's punch it would leave no trace of its fiery plunge. Our other concern was that the comet was hitting the side of Jupiter facing away from Earth, so that whatever show there was might end before the planet rotated the impact site to face Earth. Would Comet Shoemaker-Levy 9 end as T.S. Eliot wrote, in 1925, in *The Hollow Men*?

> *This is the way the world ends*
> *This is the way the world ends*
> *This is the way the world ends*
> *Not with a bang but a whimper.*[152]

Finally, late in the afternoon of July 16, the good news came briskly from Europe. Observers at a telescope in Spain had seen a major explosion on Jupiter: lasting the better part of an hour, the convulsion was as bright—in the filter they used—as one of Jupiter's moons. A few hours later, the Hubble Space Telescope sent down images of a huge fireball arcing over the planet, followed by a dark cloud a quarter the size of Earth. We were in the midst of a press conference when the ecstatic astronomers a floor below received these pictures. One of these astronomers, Heidi Hammel, broke into our press conference holding a picture in one hand and a bottle of champagne in the other, and the world watched as the audience of reporters cheered this stunning news. After the press conference, we visited the observation support system room, one floor below, where images of the new dark spot left by Fragment A were displayed, and then we drove to the U.S. Naval Observatory in Washington, 50 miles away, where we looked at Jupiter through one of the great refractor telescopes there. July 16, 1994, was an unforgettable night.

As one fragment after another struck Jupiter, impact week grew in excitement. Fragment G, a hunk of ice and dust perhaps a kilometer across, struck Jupiter on July 18, leaving a cloud larger than the Earth. It was the most conspicuous marking ever seen on another planet. By the end of impact week, Jupiter lay bombarded with these dark clouds, markings that remained visible for almost a year.

> *Thou too, O Comet beautiful and fierce,*
> *Who drew the heart of this frail Universe*
> *Towards thine own; till, wrecked in that convulsion,*
> *Alternating attraction and repulsion,*
> *Thine went astray and that was rent in twain;*
> *Oh, float into our azure heaven again!*

Percy Bysshe Shelley, *Epipsychidion*, 1821[153]

A LESSON IN OUR HERITAGE

Although the real lessons of this extraordinary event took a while to emerge, it was evident right away that we had experienced the most fundamental of events in our solar system. Impacts are the means by which the Earth and the other planets were originally put together from basic building blocks. However, the primordial Earth was too hot for any of the building blocks for life to assemble there: no carbon, hydrogen, oxygen, or nitrogen. These materials were still intact only among the distant outer worlds of the solar system, and without any way to get them here, life would never have started on Earth. It is possible that comets, rich in these materials, provided the delivery service for the building blocks of life, both through direct crashes with Earth and through the tiny specks of dust comets leave behind, cometary particles that slowly wafted down through the atmosphere. That comets can deposit the hydrogen and oxygen of water directly into a planetary atmosphere has now been proven, for several telescopes detected, high in Jupiter's atmosphere, deposits of water from Comet Shoemaker-Levy 9.

It is a happy coincidence that the leading scientist of impact theory, Eugene Shoemaker, was one of the discoverers of the comet that collided with Jupiter. His career began when he was mapping the early nuclear bomb craters near Las Vegas, Nevada, sites that gave him the idea that some of the great natural craters on Earth and on the Moon might be the results of impacts. In the mid-1950s, he established that the crater near Flagstaff, Arizona, was the result of the crash of an asteroid from space some 50,000 years ago. He later established the impact nature of most of the craters we see on the Moon. Shoemaker is a strong believer in the idea that the reason life exists here on Earth is that, when comets struck the Earth billions of years ago, they delivered the building blocks of life. "We are the progeny of comets," says Shoemaker, whose dream has been to see an impact taking place somewhere on Earth, and then rush out to map the new crater. He never thought that his dream would be realized so dramatically, on another world, by a comet he helped discover. It was a collision that brought home the incredible power of comet impacts to bring—and to take away—life on Earth.

Some say the world will end in fire,
Some say in ice.

From what I've tasted of desire
I hold with those who favor fire.
But if it had to perish twice,
I think I know enough of hate
To say that for destruction ice
Is also great
And would suffice.

Robert Frost, *Fire and Ice*, 1923[154]

AFTERMATH

By the end of Comet Shoemaker-Levy 9's impact week, Jupiter had suffered 21 major explosions as the fragments struck at the average rate of one every six hours, interrupting the ebb and flow of Jupiter's atmosphere like the rebounding hail on the rocks of *Kubla Khan*:

In Xanadu did Kubla Khan
A stately pleasure dome decree:
Where Alph, the sacred river, ran
Through caverns measureless to man
Down to a sunless sea…
And from this chasm, with ceaseless turmoil seething,
As if this earth in fast thick pants were breathing,
A mighty fountain momently was forced:
Amid whose swift half-intermitted burst
Huge fragments vaulted like rebounding hail,
Or chaffy grain beneath the thresher's flail:
And 'mid these dancing rocks at once and ever
It flung up momently the sacred river.[155]

After that incredible week of impacts, I returned home to see the large, black impact sites through Echo, the same telescope through which my parents and I first looked at Jupiter 34 years earlier. The telescope was still working well, and Mother enjoyed viewing the impacts with me. Dad, however, could not, for he had died nine years earlier from Alzheimer's disease. Looking through that telescope, I saw a planet vastly different, and suddenly I missed my father very much. Even though Dad had been a cautious person, wanting his family to make secure choices rather than chancy ones, he would have been pleased that my teenage decision to begin a life-long search for comets had worked out so well.

> *Two roads diverged in a yellow wood,*
> *And sorry I could not travel both*
> *And be one traveler, long I stood*
> *And looked down one as far as I could*
> *To where it bent in the undergrowth;*
> *Then took the other, as just as fair,*
> *And having perhaps the better claim,*
> *Because it was grassy and wanted wear;*
> *Though as for that the passing there*
> *Had worn them really about the same,*
> *And both that morning equally lay*
> *In leaves no step had trodden black.*
> *Oh, I kept the first for another day!*
> *Yet knowing how way leads on to way,*
> *I doubted if I should ever come back.*
> *I shall be telling this with a sigh*
> *Somewhere ages and ages hence:*
> *Two roads diverged in a wood, and I—*
> *I took the one less traveled by,*
> *And that has made all the difference.*[156]

R. Frost, *The Road Not Taken*, 1916

Anyone who saw Jupiter in the two months following the S-L 9 impacts could see that the planet looked changed in a way I had not seen in all my years of observing Jupiter. Scholars who studied the history of Jupiter observations since Galileo first examined the planet with a telescope in 1610 agreed that with the possible exceptions of black spots observed by Gian Cassini[157] in 1690 and Johann Schröter in 1785, humans had not seen an event like this before.[158] It was as though we were looking at a new Jupiter,

> *changed, changed utterly:*
> *A terrible beauty is born.*[159]

The planet seemed physically altered, not politically as Yeats wrote in *Easter 1916*. Great dark spots much larger than Earth covered the southern part of the planet, and as the weeks passed Jupiter's upper atmosphere winds began to merge them into a single black band. The new structures persisted almost a year; I could still detect a faint dark band in June of 1995. That month I told the story of Shoemaker-Levy 9 and Jupiter to a group of life insurance salesmen known as the Million Dollar Round Table. There I painted a picture of a comet as a sailing ship coming to the end of a Ulyssian odyssey that had been going on for 4.5 billion years. At the end of my talk, Ken Medema, a piano improvisationist, played a song with words and music that pierced the heart of what I had been trying to say about Shoemaker-Levy 9. He could have played about the comet's breakup, its collision, or even the big fireballs that arched over Jupiter. But instead he captured my wish that my father could have seen the wondrous event of a dying 4.5 billion-year-old comet. It was not so much a death, not so much a crash, as it was the docking of a sailing ship on the shore of a mighty world.

> *Daddy come look in the evening sky*
> *At the edge of tomorrow's dawn:*
> *It's four billion years old;*
> *It's a mighty ship*
> *That goes sailing on and on.*

> *Daddy come look in the evening sky*
> *For the wonder's yet to come;*
> *And follow the course*
> *Of that great sailing ship,*
> *Til the ship comes sailing home.*[160]

Endnotes

ENDNOTES *to the* TEXT

1. Leslie C. Peltier, *Starlight Nights* (New York: Random House, 1965) 231.
2. Robert Frost, "A Star in a Stone-Boat," *Robert Frost: Collected Poems, Prose, and Plays*, ed. Richard Poirier and Mark Richardson (New York: Library of America, 1995) 162.
3. John Donne, *Go and Catch a Falling Star, in Poems and Prose* (Everyman's Library of Alfred Knopf, 1995) 14.
4. George Gordon, Lord Byron, "Manfred," (Act 1, scene 1) *Lord Byron: Selected Poems and Letters*, ed. William H. Marshall (Boston: Houghton Mifflin, 1968) 232.
5. Robert Southey, "St. Antidius, the Pope and the Devil," *The Poetical Works of Robert Southey, with a memoir of the author* (Boston: Little Brown, 1863) 147.
6. John Denver, "Rocky Mountain High," *Rocky Mountain High* (New York: RCA records, 1972).
7. John Denver, *Take Me Home: An Autobiography* (New York: Harmony Books, 1994) 109-110.
8. Frost, "Aquainted with the Night," *Collected Poems* 234.
9. Samuel Taylor Coleridge, "The Rime of the Ancient Mariner," (IV) *English Romantic Poetry and Prose*, ed. Russell Noyes (New York: Oxford University Press, 1956) 396.
10. Gerard Manley Hopkins, "A fragment of anything you like," *The Poetical Works of Gerard Manley Hopkins*, ed. Norman H. MacKenzie (Oxford: Clarendon Press, 1990) 11.
11. Thomas Gray, "Journal of a Tour Through the English Lakes," *The Poetry of Earth: A Collection of English Nature Writings*, ed. Edward Dudley Hume Johnson (New York: Athenaeum, 1974) 51-52.
12. Coleridge, "Anima Poetae," *The Poetry of Earth* 129.
13. Hopkins, *The Journals and Papers of Gerard Manley Hopkins*, ed. Humphrey House and Graham Storey (London: Oxford University Press, 1959) 218.
14. James Kinsley, *The Oxford Book of Ballads* (Oxford: Clarendon Press, 1969) 312.
15. Coleridge, "Ancient Mariner," (Part III) *English Romantic Poetry and Prose* 395.
16. William Shakespeare, *Othello*, act II, scene iii, lines 177-180. *William Shakespeare: The Complete Works* ed. Peter Alexander (London: Tudor Edition of Collins, 1951, 1964).
17. Shakespeare, *King Lear*, I, ii, 1-2, 101.
18. *King Lear*, I, ii, 115.

19. *The Sonnets of William Shakespeare*, ed. Robert Ballou (New York: Avenel Books, 1961) 59.

20. John Milton, "Samson Agonistes," (line 80) *The Norton Anthology of English Literature*, ed. Meyer Howard Abrams (New York: W.W. Norton, 1968) 706.

21. Milton, "Paradise Lost," I (line 594) *Paradise Lost and Selected Poetry and Prose*, ed. Northrop Frye (New York: Holt, Rinehart and Winston, 1951) 21-22.

22. Thomas Hardy, *The Collected Poems of Thomas Hardy* (New York: Macmillan, 1926) 105-106.

23. John Keats, "Bright Star," *English Romantic Poetry and Prose* 1189.

24. Stephen Crane, "A Man Said to the Universe," *The American Tradition in Literature*, vol. 2, ed. Sculley Bradley, Richmond Beatty, and E. Hudson Long, (New York: Norton, 1967) 944.

25. Max Ehrmann, *The Poems of Max Ehrmann*, ed. Bertha Pratt Ehrmann (Boston: Boston Crescendo, 1948) 83.

26. Frost, "Stars," *Collected Poems* 19.

27. Poirier and Richardson, 942.

28. Frost, "Two Tramps in Mud Time," *Collected Poems* 252.

29. Frost, "Choose Something Like a Star," *Collected Poems* 365.

30. Frost, "Astrometaphysical," *Collected Poems* 352.

31. *I Chronicles* 21:16.

32. *Amos*, 8:9, translation from *The Holy Scriptures According to the Masoretic Text* (Philadelphia: Jewish Publication Society, 1917, rpt. 1955) 51.

33. *Isaiah*, 38:8.

34. Geoffrey Chaucer, "The Miller's Tale," (line 3458) *The Works of Geoffrey Chaucer*, ed. Fred Norris Robinson (Boston: Houghton Mifflin, 1957).

35. Shakespeare, *Julius Caesar*, II, ii, 31.

36. Shakespeare, *All's Well That Ends Well*, I, i, 178-192.

37. Majorie Hope Nicolson, "The Discovery of Space," *Medieval and Renaissance Studies*, ed. O.B. Hardison, Jr. (Chapel Hill: University of North Carolina Press, 1966).

38. Theodore Ritter von Oppolzer, *Canon of Eclipses* (rpt. New York: Dover, 1962) charts 131-134, lunar eclipse table, 368.

39. Shakespeare, *Antony and Cleopatra*, III, xiii, 152-154.

40. Shakespeare, *Hamlet*, II, ii, 115-118.

41. Marvin Spevack, *A Complete and Systematic Concordance to the Works of Shakespeare* (Hildesheim: Georg Olms, 1968).

42. Wolfgang H. Clemen, *The Development of Shakespeare's Imagery* (London: Methuen and Co., 1951) 93.

43. *King Lear*, I, ii, 133-143.

44. J.W. Draper, "Shakespeare's Star-crossed Lovers," *Review of English Studies* 15 (1939) 20.

45. W.D. Smith, "The Elizabethan Rejection of Judicial Astrology and Shakespeare's Practice," *Shakespeare Quarterly* 9 (1958) 159-176.
46. Shakespeare, *The Two Gentlemen of Verona*, II, v, 73-75.
47. Shakespeare, *Richard II*, II, iv, 7-11.
48. *Hamlet*, I, i, 114-120.
49. Shakespeare, *Henry VIII*, IV, i, 49-55.
50. Shakespeare, *1 Henry IV*, I, ii, 12-15.
51. Shakespeare, *2 Henry IV*, II, iv, 177.
52. *King Lear*, I, v, 33-36.
53. *Julius Caesar*, I, ii, 139-141.
54. Shakespeare, *Macbeth*, I, iv, 50-51.
55. *Macbeth*, II, I, 4-5.
56. *Julius Caesar*, III, I, 60-62.
57. *King Lear*, I, ii, 123.
58. Johnstone Parr, *Tamburlaine's Malady and other Essays on Astrology in Elizabethan Drama* (University, Alabama: University of Alabama Press, 1953) 80-81.
59. *Romeo and Juliet*, IV, v, 94-95.
60. Shakespeare, *Troilus and Cressida*, I, iii, 85-94.
61. Robert Walker, "The Celestial Plane in Shakespeare," *Shakespeare Survey* 8 (1955) 109-117.
62. *Oxford English Dictionary* suggests that the first such use was in Edward Blount's 1600 translation of a work by Conestaggio about the end of the House of Portugall. See Conestaggio, G., *The historie of the uniting of the kingdom of Portugall to the crown of Castill*, trans. E. Blount (London: A. Hatfield, 1600).
63. Sir John Davies, *Orchestra, or A Poem of Dancing*, ed. Eustace M.W. Tillyard (London: Chatto and Windus, 1947) 27.
64. *Orchestra*, 25.
65. Francis Bacon, "Of Seditions and Troubles," *Essays or Counsels Civil and Moral of Francis Bacon* (London: Collins, date unlisted) 130.
66. Bacon, "Of Superstition," 157.
67. Jean-Marie Pousseur, *Bacon, 1561-1626: Inventer la science* (Paris: Belin, 1988)
68. John Donne, "The First Anniversary," (lines 205-218) *The Poems of John Donne*, ed. Sir Robert Grierson (London: Oxford University Press, 1933) vol. 1, 237-238.
69. Donne, "Ignatius His Conclave," *Donne: Poems and Prose* (New York: Everyman's Library of Alfred Knopf, 1995) 199-203.
70. Henry More, "The Argument of Democritus Platonissans, or The Infinity of Worlds," (Verse 24) *Philosophical Poems* (Cambridge: Roger Daniel, printer to the University, 1647, rpt. Scolar Press, 1969) 197.
71. William Wordsworth, "Star Gazers," *Wordswoth: Selected Poems*, ed. Herschel M. Margoliouth (London: Collins, 1959) 469.
72. Alfred, Lord Tennyson, "In Memoriam" (CVI, lines 1-8) *Victorian Poetry and*

Poetics, ed. Walter E. Houghton and G. Robert Stange (Boston: Houghton Mifflin Co., 1968) 76.

73. Tennyson, "The Princess: Now Sleeps the Crimson Petal," (lines 7-10) *Victorian Poetry and Poetics* 44.
74. Milton Millhauser, *Fire and Ice: The Influence of Science on Tennyson's Poetry* (Lincoln: The Tennyson Society, Tennyson Research Center, 1971) 19.
75. *Victorian Poetry and Poetics* 6.
76. Tennyson, "In Memoriam," (CXIV, lines 1-4) *Victorian Poetry and Poetics* 78.
77. "In Memoriam," (CXX, 5-8) *Poetics* 80.
78. J.W. Pearce, *In Memoriam* (New York: Macmillan, 1912) xl.
79. K. W. Gransden, "The Poet and the Age," *Tennyson: In Memoriam* (London: Edward Arnold Publishers, 1964) 11, 19.
80. "In Memoriam," (V, 1-4) *Poetics* 46.
81. "In Memoriam," (XXXIV, 5-8) *Poetics* 54.
82. "In Memoriam," (LXXXIX, 43-52) *Poetics* 69-70.
83. "In Memoriam," (III, 1-16) *Poetics* 46.
84. "In Memoriam," (LVI, 9-20), *Poetics* 59-60.
85. Hopkins, "Nondum," *The Poetical Works of Gerard Manley Hopkins*, 91-92, 289. I thank Dr. Norman MacKenzie for suggesting to me this similarity of thought between Hopkins and Tennyson.
86. Millhauser 19.
87. "In Memoriam," (CXXVIII, 5-6) *Poetics* 82.
88. "In Memoriam," (XXI, 17-20) *Poetics* 51.
89. Satellite data from J. Kelly Beatty, Brian O'Leary, and Andrew Chaikin, *The New Solar System* (Cambridge, MA: Sky Publishing, 1980), 220.
90. "In Memoriam," (XXIV, 1-4) *Poetics* 51.
91. "In Memoriam," (XXXIII, 13-16) *Poetics* 51.
92. "In Memoriam," (LIV, 1-20) *Poetics* 59.
93. "In Memoriam," (CXVIII, 1-28) *Poetics* 79.
94. Tennyson, "Maud," (lines 136-143) *Poetics* 91.
95. "In Memoriam," (CXXIII, 1-8) *Poetics* 81.
96. *Ecclesiastes* 1:7. Although some sources suggest that Solomon himself authored *Ecclesiastes*, Martin Luther and others date the book to a later author. However, since fragments of the text were found at Qumran, it could not have been dated later than 150 BC. See C. Ryrie, *The Ryrie Study Bible* (Chicago: Moody Press, 1976).
97. "In Memoriam," (CXXI, 1-4, 9-12, 17-20) *Poetics* 80.
98. Tennyson, "Locksley Hall," (lines 7-10) *Poetics* 33.
99. Matthew Arnold, "A Summer Night," (lines 76-92) *Poetics* 446.
100. This chapter is adapted from my thesis, *The Starlight Night: Hopkins and Astronomy* (Department of English: Queen's University, 1979); and subsequent

paper "Gerard Manley Hopkins and Some Mid-19th Century Comets," *Journal of the Royal Astronomical Society of Canada* 75, No. 3 (1981) 139-150.

101. The weather conditions from that night were from the *London Times*, August 4, 1864. Solar system data is courtesy of Michael Payette, and was checked using *The Sky* Graphical Astronomy Software Version 1.04 (Golden, Colo.: Software Bisque, 1992).

102. MacKenzie 40.

103. MacKenzie, 244-246, personal communication.

104. *Cornhill*, October 1862, 550-551.

105. *London Times*, 1 August 1864, 5e.

106. *London Review*, 13 July 1861, 44.

107. *London Times*, 3 July 1861, 5e.

108. Amedée Guillemin, *The World of Comets*, trans. James Glaisher et al. (London: Sampson Low, 1877) 254-255.

109. *Judges* 6: 36-37.

110. Guillemin 314.

111. MacKenzie 40.

112. Guillemin 32.

113. J. Russell Hind, *The Comet of 1556; being popular replies to every-day questions, referring to its anticipated reappearance, with some observations on the apprehension of danger from comets* (London: John W. Parker and Son, 1857) 1.

114. Hind 14.

115. *London Times*, 4 July 1861, 12; repeated verbatim in *Illustrated London News*, 6 July 1861, 3.

116. J.R. Hind, *The Comet of 1556*.

117. Hopkins, *The Journals and Papers of Gerard Manley Hopkins*, (entry for 13 July 1874) ed. Humphrey House and Graham Storey (London: Oxford University Press) 249.

118. Hopkins, *Further Letters of Gerard Manley Hopkins Including his Correspondence with Coventry Patmore*, (letter of December 1878) ed. Claude C. Abbott (London: Oxford University Press, 1956) 135-136.

119. *Further Letters* 137.

120. Coventry Patmore, *Poems* (London: George Bell, 1906) 255.

121. *Further Letters* 317.

122. Brian Marsden, "The Sungrazing Comet Group," *Astronomical Journal* 72 (1967) 1179.

123. Henry David Thoreau, *The Heart of Thoreau's Journals*, ed. Odell Shepard (New York: Houghton Mifflin, 1927) undated entry.

124. Ralph Waldo Emerson, "The American Scholar," *Selected Essays, Lectures, and Poems*, ed. Robert Richardson (New York: Bantam, 1990) 84.

125. Emerson, "Self-Reliance," *Selected Essays* 155.

126. Thoreau, *Journals*, undated, 1840s.
127. Thoreau, *Walden* (New York: Peebles Press International, date unlisted) 7-8.
128. Venus data was accessed through *The Sky* Graphical Astronomy Software.
129. Thoreau, *Walden* 23, 76.
130. Thoreau, *Journals*, 26 July 1840, 24.
131. Thoreau, *Journals*, 19 April 1854, 194.
132. Thoreau, *Journals*, 13 September 1852, 149-150.
133. William Graves Hoyt, *Planets X and Pluto* (Tucson: University of Arizona Press, 1980), 12.
134. Hoyt 15.
135. Thoreau, *Journals*, 13 September 1852, 149-150.
136. Thoreau, *Journals*, 13 February 1852, 118-120.
137. Thoreau, *Journals*, 18 February 1852, 120.
138. Walt Whitman, "When I Heard the Learn'd Astronomer," *The American Tradition in Literature*, vol. 2, 102.
139. Thoreau, *Journals*, 4 October 1859, 322.
140. Thoreau, *Journals*, 28 October 1852, 151.
141. Milton, "Paradise Lost" (IV, line 208) *Paradise Lost and Selected Poetry and Prose* 85.
142. "Paradise Lost," (IV, 248-251) *Paradise* 86.
143. "Paradise Lost," (IV, 604-609) *Paradise* 96.
144. Tennyson, "Ulysses," *Poetics* 31.
145. W.B. Yeats, "The Second Coming," *Collected Poems of W.B. Yeats* (London: Macmillan, 1977) 210.
146. Thoreau, *Walden* 285, 287.
147. Shakespeare, *Othello*, V, ii, 107.
148. Tennyson, "Morte d'Arthur," (lines 11-12) *Poetics* 28.
149. Frost, "Kitty Hawk," *Collected Poems* 445.
150. Eugene M Shoemaker to Brian G. Marsden, 26 March 1993.
151. Keats, "On First Looking into Chapmans's Homer," *English Romantic Poetry and Prose*, 1129.
152. T.S. Eliot, "The Hollow Men," *Collected Poems: 1909-1062* (London: Faber and Faber, 1974) 92.
153. Percy Bysshe Shelley, "Epipsychidion," (lines 368-373) *Selected Poetry and Prose of Shelley*, ed. Carlos Baker (New York: Modern Library of Random House, 1951) 283.
154. Frost, "Fire and Ice," *Collected Poems* 204.
155. Coleridge, "Kubla Khan," *English Romantic Poetry and Prose* 391. Coleridge wrote this poem in 1797 after experiencing a hallucination from two grains of opium taken to control an attack of dysentery.
156. Frost, "The Road Not Taken," *Collected Poems* 103.

157. Stephen James O'Meara, "Schröter and Jupiter's Dark Spots," *Sky and Telescope* 92, No. 1 (1996) 98-100.

158. J. Kelly Beatty, "A Comet Crash in 1690?" *Sky and Telescope* 93, No. 4 (1997) 111.

159. Yeats, "Easter 1916," *Collected Poems* 205. The poem commemorates the Irish rebellion of Easter Sunday of that year; the British executed the people named in the poem.

> *I write it out in a verse—*
> *MacDonagh and MacBride*
> *And Connolly and Pearse*
> *Now and in time to be,*
> *Wherever green is worn,*
> *Are changed, changed utterly:*
> *A terrible beauty is born.*

160. Ken Medema, "Daddy come look in the evening sky," Million Dollar Round Table conference, June 1995.

ENDNOTES *to the* ILLUSTRATIONS

A. Jane Taylor, *Rhymes for the Nursery* (London: Darton and Harvey, 1806) 10-11.

B. Alfred, Lord Tennyson, "Vastness," *The Poems of Tennyson*, ed. Christopher Ricks (New York: W.W. Norton, 1969) 1346.

C. Samuel Taylor Coleridge, "Dejection: An Ode," *English Romantic Poetry and Prose* 418.

D. Emily Dickinson, *The Complete Poems of Emily Dickinson*, ed. Thomas H. Johnson (Boston: Little, Brown, 1890, 1960) 130.

E. George Meredith, "Lucifer in Starlight," *Victorian Poetry and Poetics* 651.

F. Frederick Langbridge, "A Cluster of Quiet Thoughts," (Religious Tract Society Publication) *Oxford Dictionary of Quotations* (London: Oxford University Press, 1955) 310.

G. Dickinson, *Complete Poems* 642.

H. Robert Frost, "The Star-Splitter," *Collected Poems* 166.

I. Edward Young, *Selected Poems*, ed. B. Hepworth (Cheadle, England: Fyfield Books, 1975), 93-94.

J. Dickinson, *Complete Poems* 408-409.

K. Bayard Taylor, *The Poems* (Boston: Ticknor and Fields, 1866) 134-135.

L. Tennyson, "In Memoriam," (XXIV, 3-4) *Poetics* 51

M. Tennyson, "Move Eastward, Happy Earth," *Poetics* 42.

N. Ralph Waldo Emerson, "The Informing Spirit," *The Poems of Ralph Waldo Emerson* (New York: The Heritage Press, 1945) 183.

O.   Andrew Marvell, "The Definition of Love," *Renaissance England: Poetry and Prose from the Reformation to the Restoration* (New York: W.W. Norton, 1956) 997.

P.   Sir Charles Roberts, *The Collected Poems of Sir Charles G.D. Roberts*, ed. Desmond Pacey (Wolfville, N.S.: Wombat, 1985) 120

Q.   William Wordsworth, "I wandered lonely as a cloud," *English Romantic Poetry and Prose* 324-325.

R.   *Psalms* 121:1.

S.   Emerson, "Society and Solitude," *The Complete Works of Ralph Waldo Emerson*, vol. 7 (New York: AMS Press, 1979) 28.

T.   George Meredith, "Modern Love," *The Oxford Dictionary of Quotations* 336.

U.   Milton, "Paradise Lost," (VIII, 76-84) *Paradise* 180.

V.   Edward FitzGerald, "The Rubáiyát of Omar Khayyám of Naishápúr," *Victorian Poetry and Poetics* 343.

W.   Oscar Wilde, *Lady Windermere's Fan* (London: Eyre Methuen, 1964, 1978) 51.

X.   Shakespeare, *1 Henry VI*, I, i, 1-7.

Index